GROWING PLANTS IN
NUTRIENT SOLUTIONS

King Cardinal carnations growing in nutrients. Benched in July; photographed in December. Note exceptional foliage and abundance of buds. Flowers 5 inches in diameter and with 48-inch stems were cut from these plants.

GROWING PLANTS IN NUTRIENT SOLUTIONS

or

Scientifically Controlled Growth

BY

WAYNE I. TURNER

AND

VICTOR M. HENRY

NEW YORK

JOHN WILEY & SONS, Inc.

LONDON: CHAPMAN & HALL, LIMITED

8¢

Second Printing, November, 1945

PRINTED IN U. S. A.

TO

Our professors, associates, and friends at the University of Illinois, who so conscientiously instilled in us the fundamental knowledge which made this book possible, and to all commercial growers of America, with the hope that they will go forward with confidence in this new science, we humbly dedicate this book.

PREFACE

Those persons interested in nutrient culture fall quite naturally into three classes: those who are merely interested from a curiosity standpoint and are intrigued by this fascinating subject; those who recognize its commercial possibilities and want a simple practical method that has been proven; and those who are interested in research work and have contributed so materially to the subject. We believe that this book will have some appeal for each class. For those men who are doing research work, we hope that this volume will bring together various ideas, formulas, and theories which have been established. We do not attempt to promote any radically new theories, nor do we claim as original most of the methods outlined.

We do believe that the practical results obtained through this work will encourage commercial producers to improve this method of controlled growing and truly show its real possibilities. We sincerely hope that the chapters on practical greenhouse conversion, methods of control, and definite formulas will embolden the many growers who have hesitated heretofore to adopt this method of culture. We are certain they will find that they can grow finer flowers and vegetables with much less trouble and at a greater profit. Those persons who may be classed as advanced amateurs will find that, by studying the chapters on practical greenhouse culture, they will be able to adapt the ideas on window-box and small-tank culture to their own problems. This is admirably illustrated by the three color plates showing actual results of such an amateur-installation.

The purpose of the book is to give a practical working knowledge of the various methods of growing plants in nutrient solutions. We believe that we have presented the subject in sufficiently non-technical language so that the layman or the person with only a limited knowledge of chemistry or botany will find no difficulty in following our methods.

WAYNE I. TURNER
VICTOR M. HENRY

March, 1939.

ACKNOWLEDGMENT

Although the information in this book is drawn to a great extent from the actual experience of Mr. Turner, the various methods of construction, the tests, and the formulas are compiled from the many excellent bulletins and articles issued by the several state experiment stations which have pioneered in this work. We especially want to acknowledge our indebtedness to the research workers of the New Jersey Experiment Station; the Purdue University Experiment Station; the Ohio State University Experiment Station; the Central Experimental Farm, Ottawa, Canada; and the University of Illinois Experiment Station. We have drawn freely from many of the available articles appearing in trade journals when we thought the information reliable. Wherever possible the source has been credited. We are grateful for all such articles.

We are sincerely indebted to the following persons for their writings, helpful suggestions, or sincere criticism of our ideas: H. M. Biekart, C. H. Connors, Robert Withrow, E. E. DeTurk, S. F. Thornton, S. D. Conner, R. R. Fraser, I. C. Hoffman, E. W. McElwee, M. A. Blake, G. T. Nightingale, O. W. Davidson, D. A. Magraw, C. W. Kearns, H. Hill, M. B. Davis, R. P. White, R. B. Farnham, L. C. Chadwick, Arnold Wagner, J. H. Hanley, W. F. Gericke, and John Arthur.

We particularly wish to thank F. F. Weinard, of the Floricultural Experiment Station, University of Illinois, for suggestions and criticism of the completed manuscript. To R. H. Bray of the University of Illinois and to A. L. Whiting of the Urbana Laboratories we are especially indebted for the directions in the chapter entitled "Testing Nutrient Solutions."

WAYNE I. TURNER
March, 1939.   VICTOR M. HENRY

CONTENTS

GROWING PLANTS IN NUTRIENT SOLUTIONS

CHAPTER I

A GENERAL VIEW OF NUTRIENT CULTURE

The idea of growing plants without soil is not new. Originally it was employed in physiological experiments only, but recently it has been proved to be thoroughly practical and also to have some very definite advantages over ordinary culture in soil.

Many different terms are used to describe this way of growing plants, for several different methods are practical from a commercial standpoint. Some of these terms are hydroponics, sand culture, water culture, cinder culture, chemiculture, tank farming, and soilless agriculture. The major differences are indicated in the terms themselves. We shall not attempt to cover in detail all these methods, but we shall call attention to the important differences and show the practical superiority of several. Nutrient solution culture, or, for the sake of simplicity, "nutrient culture," is a descriptive term which we prefer and shall use throughout this discussion for uniformity. By this term we shall refer to all methods of growing plants without soil and supplying the nutrients artificially in solution.

It is only natural that a subject of this sort would attract the attention of scientists. Scores of men have worked on the problems involved since the idea was conceived a hundred or more years ago. It would be almost impossible and certainly not within the scope of this book to attempt to mention all the well-known men who have contributed materially to the subject. However, certain men have done outstanding work in this field, particularly from the standpoint of taking it out of the experimental class and showing its practicability in the commercial field.

Those interested in growing vegetables and flowers should feel indebted to such men as H. M. Biekart and C. H. Connors, of the New Jersey Experiment Station; W. F. Gericke, formerly of the University of California; and Robert Withrow, of Purdue University, because

FIG. 1. An average cluster of tomatoes growing in nutrients. Planted in September; photographed in early December. Note uniformity of size and perfect shape. This is not an unusual cluster, as some had as many as twelve fruits.

each has made noteworthy contributions with respect both to the scientific phase and to the practical adaptation from a commercial standpoint. Biekart and Connors of New Jersey have been growing carnations and roses for eight or ten years on a commercial scale by the nutrient-culture method in sand. W. F. Gericke has received country-wide recognition for his work, particularly in the growing of such crops as tomatoes, potatoes, corn, beans, and miscellaneous vegetables.

To Withrow, of Purdue, should go a great deal of credit for developing a practical subirrigation system that is peculiarly adapted to large-scale commercial growing.

The Original New Jersey Method

Each of these men uses a different yet successful method of supporting the plants and applying the nutrient solution. The method used by Biekart and Connors employed the regular greenhouse bench filled with clean sand instead of soil. The required nutrients were supplied by mixing the necessary chemicals in an elevated tank of water and applying this solution with a hose (by gravity flow) in the same way benches of soil are watered. The plants were fed in this way several times a week, and between periods of feeding the sand was kept moist with ordinary tap water. Whenever necessary, usually every two or three weeks, the sand was thoroughly leached with water to remove any accumulations of chemicals.

It is evident that this method, since it does not require any change in bench construction and necessitates only the addition of an overhead mixing tank, is an economical method to start nutrient-solution experiments. The disadvantage of this procedure, however, is that a great amount of the valuable chemical salts is lost in draining the excess solution out of the bench and by the leaching process. Furthermore, there is no saving in the labor of watering, as this is still done by hand. Another objection to the original New Jersey sand-culture system is that the sand must be free of limestone. In many sections of the country sand which is free of lime is hard to obtain and expensive. Sand containing a high percentage of limestone requires the addition of too much acid to bring the acidity to the proper range for the growing of many crops. We find that the acidity of the nutrient solution is of great importance, and we take very definite steps to keep it within the proper range. Possibly with such a crop as sweet peas, a sand containing lime would be satisfactory. Certainly much trouble

Fig. 2. General view of carnations growing in nutrients. House in foreground King Cardinal; house at right Vivian. Houses 190 feet by 27 feet.

would be experienced with a crop like gardenias. Several years ago New Jersey abandoned this method for an improved subirrigation system designed by R. B. Farnham.

W. F. GERICKE'S METHOD

Dr. Gericke's method is more simple in some respects, as the roots of the plants grow in and are in constant contact with the nutrient solution. With his method, waterproof benches are constructed of any suitable material. (Details of construction of a waterproof bench will be given later.) Coarse wire netting or hardware cloth is stretched over the top of these benches, and on this is laid burlap, coarse shavings, excelsior, or similar material. This netting and excelsior help to support the growing plants. In contrast to the original New Jersey sand-culture method it will be seen that this system is more expensive in first cost because it is necessary to make the benches waterproof. However, there is a definite saving in chemicals and fertilizers, since none of the valuable salts are lost through the benches. There is, of course, a further saving in that hand watering is eliminated. Some growers who are using this system have found it advantageous to add a pump to circulate the solution continuously. This, of course, adds another item of expense. One disadvantage of this method is the practical necessity of getting sufficient air to the roots of the plants since they are constantly immersed in the nutrient solution. As the reader probably knows, it is difficult to make water absorb air; this absorption must be accomplished by some mechanical process such as agitating the solution vigorously, keeping it in constant circulation by pumping the solution into a tower and allowing it to fall by gravity over some sort of grating to aerate it, or by actually forcing air into the solution with an air pump. Although the job of getting air into the solution is not so expensive a process as may appear from the foregoing, it is not so reliable a method of getting proper aeration of the roots as either of the other two systems which we discuss. Another disadvantage of the Gericke system is that the plants are held in place insecurely and as a result the root system may be damaged during syringing. We believe that Dr. Gericke's method combined with the sunny California climate gives the largest yield we have ever seen, but we think it has a very definite disadvantage if used in those sections of the country where there are a number of consecutive cloudy days, as plants growing with their roots constantly in contact with water do not thrive under such cloudy conditions.

PRESENT NEW JERSEY METHOD

This last factor is one of the main reasons why we have adopted and recommend the third system of nutrient culture. It seems to combine all the desirable features of the other two and in addition has some important advantages. R. B. Farnham of the New Jersey Experiment Station worked out a system of waterproof benches and a subirrigation method of delivering the nutrient solution to the plants. A little later in the same year, Robert Withrow of Purdue University worked out a similar system with the solution-tank under the benches using a centrifugal pump to force the solution into the benches, and allowing it to drain back to the solution-tank by gravity. In the Middle West, at least, the system is known as the Withrow method, and certainly Withrow has done remarkable work with it and well deserves such acknowledgment.

THE WITHROW METHOD

Briefly, the system consists of waterproof benches built in much the same way as those used by Dr. Gericke with the exception that no wire cloth, burlap, or excelsior is used. Instead the benches are filled with gravel, preferably low in calcium (lime), or cinders. All greenhouse establishments that are heated with coal accumulate an excess of cinders which ordinarily are a liability, and for that reason we prefer to use cinders to save the expense of buying gravel as well as the cost of disposing of the cinders. We also find that it is easy to adjust the acidity of the solution when cinders are used.

It is of great importance to see that the benches are properly leveled. Theoretically, there should be a slight fall in the benches toward the end nearest the solution-tank which would enable the solution to drain out more rapidly and more completely. In actual construction it is easier and, so far as we have discovered, just as well to have the benches as nearly level as possible. By using a surveyor's transit, a careful workman can build a bench 100 feet long and have it within $\frac{1}{4}$ inch of level. It is of particular importance to see that there are no pockets or depressions in the bench to hold the solution. At a centrally located point and definitely lower than the benches is a waterproof concrete tank constructed to hold the nutrient solution. In a separate compartment alongside this solution-tank is located an electrically driven centrifugal pump. From the solution-tank a single run of pipe goes to each bench to be supplied from that tank. At each bench this pipe discharges under an inverted trough which rests on the bottom of the bench and extends its entire length. This inverted trough helps to distribute the solution uniformly throughout the bench. Reference to Fig. 7 will show how it operates; complete construction details will be given later.

The pump which forces the solution into the benches is operated by a time switch so that the benches are filled and emptied several times a day. It is readily seen that many very important things are accomplished automatically with this system. As the solution is forced into the benches air is forced out of the cinders, and as the solution drains from the benches air is drawn back into the cinders. This results in perfect aeration of the roots. Moreover, no valuable solution is lost because the benches are waterproof. It is not necessary to water the plants by hand, as this is accomplished by pumping the solution to them. Since all this is done mechanically with electric power and automatically by using a time switch, the entire system can be operated at very low cost once it is installed.

Chapter II

COMMERCIAL ADVANTAGES

There are many reasons why the commercial grower should be enthusiastic about the culture of flowers or vegetables in nutrient solutions. Chief among these is the fact that it is definitely cheaper. The growing of plants in nutrient solutions is much more efficient than ordinary soil culture. The plant that is being grown is fed just those elements that it needs for proper growth and development, and no others. There is no waste, either of water or of fertilizer, and there are no losses of valuable nutrients by leaching.

Every practical greenhouse man knows that one of his greatest items of expense is labor. With nutrient-solution culture the manual labor required for watering is practically eliminated, as watering is accomplished in the same operation with an electric motor and pump which is supplying nutrients to the growing plants. This is just one example of the many ways in which nutrient-solution culture is more economical than soil culture. In respect to new construction the first cost is slightly more for benches, but if the benches are built properly of concrete they will give a lifetime of service, and even if made of wood the life of a bench will be increased tremendously. The reason for this is self-evident since little if any moisture or soil acids come in contact with the wood of the bench. Therefore there is no need to spend the time and labor of repairing benches every five or six years as with those used in soil culture. Likewise, steam-pipe replacement is less, because there is no constant drip from the benches onto the pipes. This yields a double saving—less labor for repairs and less pipe for replacement.

Probably no grower knows how much profit he loses in lowered efficiency of his employees who have to work in muddy walks wearing boots. By growing plants in nutrient solutions, the dripping which ruins the best of walks is eliminated. Not only is the cost of labor and materials for repair work saved, but also the employees accomplish much more since they are not needlessly tired out from working in mud.

Two other rather expensive jobs are completely eliminated by growing plants by the nutrient-culture method. No time is required for watering, and no mulching is necessary. Both are quite serious items of expense in any greenhouse range, and, in view of the fact that both the watering and feeding are done at one time by electric power instead of with manual labor, the saving is even more apparent.

Every grower knows that it is necessary to carry an extra pipe or two in a house to keep it sufficiently warm when the watering or syringing is being done. When a crop is grown in nutrient solutions less fuel is required because it is not necessary to drive out surplus moisture during cold days when watering or syringing, as in soil culture. The elimination of these excessively moist conditions brings about further savings and makes it possible to produce a much finer-quality crop because of the lessened danger of mildew and black spot on roses, for example, and of rust or other leaf spots on carnations. Naturally the result is a further saving in the reduction of the amount of fungicides needed and the labor of applying them.

Regardless of the location of a greenhouse range a big item of expense is the soil required in soil culture. It takes time, labor, and fertilizer to prepare it for planting, and a great deal of labor to wheel it in and out of the houses. If the soil is left in the benches for several years it must be sterilized with either hot water or steam. The equipment for steam sterilization is expensive; hot-water sterilization has the objection of keeping the soil wet for long periods of time. Cinders or gravel can be used as a medium to hold the root system securely in place when growing plants in nutrient solutions. The original cost of cinders is almost negligible, and we have found them just as satisfactory as gravel. Once they are placed in the benches they may be left there for many years and are easily sterilized with acid or formaldehyde at very low cost. Formaldehyde must not be used in a house where any plants are growing.

One of the most important problems in operating a range profitably is to set out as many plants as it is possible to grow properly in the benches. When plants are grown in nutrient solutions it is possible to set them closer together because the amount of nutrients that can be supplied each plant is not limited, as it is in soil culture. Light is the chief limiting factor. About 20 per cent more plants can be grown in the same bench space by the nutrient-culture method.

From the foregoing statements it is apparent that growing plants in nutrient solutions effects very definite savings by eliminating many items of expense that are unavoidable in soil culture. Other, equally

Fɪɢ. 3. Roses growing in *soil*. Hollywood, budded stock. Benched in April; photographed five weeks later in May. Note ordinary weed growth and average height of rose plants. Before these plants produced a crop, those shown in the next picture had produced a nice crop and the second was almost ready to cut.

FIG. 4. Roses growing in *nutrients*. Hollywood, dormant budded stock, benched one week earlier than those photographed in soil in preceding picture. Note entire absence of weeds and stronger growth despite the fact that the others were started buds.

important reasons would warrant a grower's adopting this method. In growing flowers, for example, it is possible to control the intensity of color and the quality of the blossom and also to adjust the time of maximum yield of product in relation to market prices.

It costs about 10 cents per square foot to convert a house from soil culture to nutrient culture, but we find that with carnations we more than double the yield and get a finer crop that brings a better price per bloom. With roses the extra cost for conversion is absorbed in one year, and undoubtedly the yield on this crop will improve with more experience. Jonquil bulbs planted on December 7 directly in the solution, with no precooling for root formation and never planted in soil, bloomed 100 per cent with perfect flowers cut on January 31. This was a late variety—Minister Talma.

Biekart and Connors of New Jersey found that carnations grown in sand with nutrient solutions gave flowers of the same quality as those grown in soil with respect to stem length, vigor of stem, and size and keeping quality of the flowers, and that they were grown at a much lower cost than in soil. This was possible because the time involved in applying fertilizer was reduced, and weeding, watering, and cultivating were eliminated. There was also evidence that there was less disease and greater freedom from red spider due to greater control of growing conditions.

In nutrient culture outdoors, Gericke of California found that tomatoes produced fruit 60 days after planting. Gericke has produced tomatoes at the rate of 200-300 tons per acre where the normal average for unstaked field-grown plants is about 5 tons per acre. He also has produced potatoes at the rate of 2,465 bushels per acre where the average soil production was about 116 bushels per acre. Possibly this could not be duplicated in a greenhouse, where the light factor is limited, but it does show the possibilities of this method of growing when one becomes proficient.

A number of greenhouse establishments are working with nutrient solutions, both experimentally and on a practical commercial scale. Some of the growers who are using this method successfully in at least a portion of their range are:

Lindley Floral Company, Springfield, Illinois.
Watson Greenhouses, Lafayette, Indiana.
A. Washburn and Sons, Bloomington, Illinois.
Yoder Brothers, Barberton, Ohio.
Bauer and Steinkamp, Indianapolis, Indiana.
A. F. Amling Company, Maywood, Illinois.
George Ball, West Chicago, Illinois.

Wholesale Floral Company, Aurora, Illinois.
Chemical Gardens, Inc., Evanston, Illinois.
J. W. Davis Company, Terre Haute, Indiana.
Ernest Brundin, Montebello, California.
Hill Floral Products Company, Richmond, Indiana.

William A. Hansen, president of the Wholesale Floral Company, is undoubtedly the pioneer commercial grower to adopt this method of culture.

Probably the growers at these ranges would permit visitors to inspect their plants. Most of the men we have talked with have indicated that this method of culture has no particular trade secrets, but that, just as in soil culture, the successful grower has the ability to take infinite pains and to give attention to detail. No crop and no method of culture will stand neglect. Work is involved, but it is fascinating and highly remunerative if the grower will give it the necessary attention.

Note: In calculating the cost per square foot of converting from soil to nutrient culture, we figure actual bench area, excluding walks, rather than total ground area.

CHAPTER III

CONVERTING FROM SOIL TO NUTRIENT CULTURE

Most commercial growers of greenhouse crops are intensely interested in the nutrient-solution culture of plants. For this reason we are giving detailed instructions on how these growers can adapt their present houses to the method of subirrigation which we have found to be best and most practicable in the Middle West. Since the average grower will want to expend as little money as necessary, we are suggesting a method that uses as much of his present materials as possible. We have found that it costs on the average about $300 to convert a soil greenhouse 30 feet by 200 feet, in good condition, into a house for nutrient culture.

We suggest that you start with one house and that you grow just one crop or if more than one crop choose those that will grow in the same solution. When you become proficient with this, other units can be added easily and confidently. We might mention that, among the flowers, carnations, and among the vegetables, tomatoes, are very responsive and profitable in nutrient solutions.

For simplicity, we will use a typical house 30 feet by 200 feet, having five 3½-foot benches. No change in heating equipment is necessary. The benches must be level within 1 inch. The height of the benches is not important but must be uniform. Since the benches must be made watertight, it is usually cheaper to tear them out and rebuild them. However, much of the old material can be salvaged. If your benches are not warped and are in excellent condition, it may be possible to caulk or strip the cracks in the bottom and strengthen the sides with braces and thus save the expense of tearing out and rebuilding them.

Additional equipment which you will need consists of a waterproof solution-tank (built in the ground under the benches), a centrifugal pump and motor (usually installed in a small compartment alongside the tank), and a time switch and other electrical controls (usually installed in the service building for convenience).

14

In selecting the house to convert to nutrient culture, choose one that is adjacent to the next unit which you expect to add later. This will permit you to add another solution tank and use the same motor and pump for both tanks. See Fig. 5.

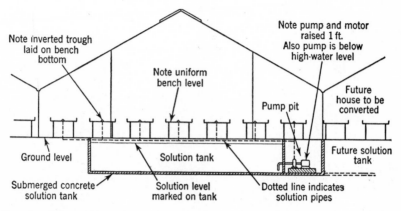

Note inverted trough laid on bench bottom

Note uniform bench level

Note pump and motor raised 1 ft. Also pump is below high-water level

Pump pit

Future house to be converted

Ground level

Solution tank

Future solution tank

Submerged concrete solution tank

Solution level marked on tank

Dotted line indicates solution pipes

FIG. 5. Cross section through center of greenhouse showing relative positions of benches, solution tank, pump, and distribution pipes.

CONSTRUCTION OF TANK

The first step is to construct the solution-tank. Before doing this, the volume of the benches to be served must be known. This we determine by multiplying the length by the depth by the width, and adding the volumes of all the benches to get the total volume. The nutrient-solution-tank must have *at least one-third* this volume. For example: if your house has five benches 3½ by 175 feet long and 6 inches deep: 5 (3½ × 175 × ½) = 1,530 cubic feet. One-third of this volume is 500 cubic feet, or the volume of the nutrient tank. Since there are 7½ gallons per cubic foot, this tank would hold 3,750 gallons. A tank approximately 5 feet by 4 feet by 25 feet will be required. It should be located in the center of the house to permit short runs of pipe to the benches. See Fig. 6. In this way, a 200-foot house can be served by pumping the solution into the center of the benches and allowing it to flow 100 feet in opposite directions. This solution-tank is constructed in the same way as a poured concrete foundation. The walls and bottom should be 4 inches thick and will not require reinforcing up to a tank capacity of 4,000 gallons or 16,000 liters. After the wooden forms are in place, see that all pipe work is placed through the walls before pouring the concrete. To insure a watertight tank it is best to pour the entire tank in one day to avoid joints that might leak. A suitable concrete mixture is composed of 1 part gray waterproof cement (or ordinary cement may be used), 2 parts medium washed sharp sand, and 4 parts washed gravel. Tamp this mixture into the forms *thoroughly* with the edge of a spade to remove voids and to insure a smooth surface for the tank. As soon as

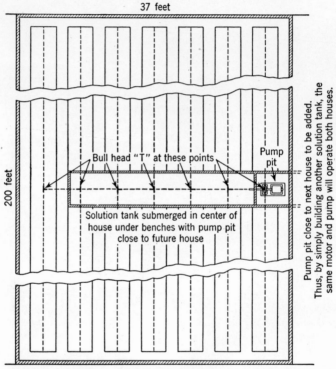

FIG. 6. Floor plan of greenhouse showing location of tank in center to permit equal runs of distributing system. Main pipe from tank to benches is run underground with riser to each bench ending in "bull-head" T.

the forms are removed from the concrete, all rough places must be patched with a mixture of 1 part waterproof cement and 2 parts fine sharp sand. Next the entire inside surface of the tank is brushed with a thin mixture of waterproof cement and silica (1 part cement, 2 parts fine silica). This can be painted on with a large paint brush and should be about the consistency of thick cream. This last process fills any tiny cracks, pits, and pores and prevents leakage. When the tank is thoroughly dry, give the inside two coats of a petroleum asphalt emulsion.* It is best to use an emulsion of the quick-break type (quick drying) containing from 40 to 60 per cent asphalt. CAUTION: *Be careful to avoid any waterproofing compounds containing coal-tar or water-gas products as they are highly toxic to plants.* This asphalt coating serves two purposes: it waterproofs the tank and it prevents the lime in the cement and gravel from neutralizing the acid in the nutrient solution. If the tank is not so coated, you will always have trouble maintaining the proper acidity. Except from the standpoint of safety it is not necessary to cover the tank. If any walks cross over it they can be bridged satisfactorily by means of two 2 inch by 10 inch boards of the proper length at each walk. You will notice from the diagram that a pump compartment is built adjoining the solution tank. This should be large enough to work in comfortably, about 5 feet by 5 feet. The pump and motor should be mounted on a metal base and raised about 1 foot off the floor of the compartment to prevent ruining the equipment should water accidentally get into this pit.

CONSTRUCTION OF BENCHES

After the solution-tank is built and tested, the next step is to build the benches. These, if made of wood, are built in much the same manner as soil benches, except that no drainage cracks are left in the bottom. Unavoidable small cracks can be caulked with oakum. All benches served from the same tank must be of uniform height and absolutely level within 1 inch. The reason for this is that we simply pump the solution to a certain height and allow it to spread through the bench by gravity. If the benches were not all the same height, one might overflow before the others were completely filled. The benches must be level since the nutrient solution drains by gravity from them into the solution-tank. There must be no pockets in which the solution collects, as it is thought that this may be one of the reasons for some of the salts precipitating from the solution and causing injury to the plants. It is advisable to use a surveyor's transit to insure uniform height and proper leveling. With such an instrument, the benches can be made level within $\frac{1}{4}$ inch per 100 feet.

The sides of the benches should be made of 6-inch material, to allow the use of 5 inches of solution in them, which is enough for the average greenhouse crop. The sides of the benches must be very rigid

* Asphalt Emulsion, United Laboratories, Cleveland, Ohio. Elastex HX, Quick Break Asphalt Emulsion, Elastic Asphalt Company, 404 North Wells Street, Chicago, Illinois.

so that they cannot be moved. We recommend bracing them, at intervals of 4 feet, with heavy wire. We use a heavy galvanized rose stake

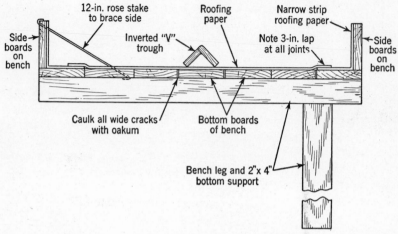

FIG. 7. Cross section of typical greenhouse bench showing method of bracing side boards, applying and lapping building paper, and position of inverted V trough.

about 12 inches long. Drive this stake through the side board about 1 inch from the top and diagonally down through the bottom of the

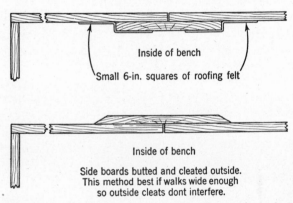

FIG. 8. Cross section of side boards on bench showing method of strengthening the butt joints with cleats and applying the small pieces of building paper to insure water-tightness.

bench. See Fig. 7. Clinch the end over the top of the side board and under the bottom of the bench. Later, when applying the asphalt waterproofing, these wires must be thoroughly coated to avoid contact with the solution. All joints where side boards butt together must be reinforced on the inside of the bench with a piece of lumber 6 inches by 12 inches, allowing a 6-inch lap on each side of the joint. See Fig. 8.

The next step is to run the pipes from the solution tank to each bench. At the point where the solution enters the bench, the discharge opening should be not less than ¾ inch. If the solution is brought in at the end of the bench a ¾-inch elbow is used, and if it is brought in at the center of the bench a ¾ by 1 by ¾ "bull-head" T is used. Depending upon the extent of the installation, the pipe and fittings are increased in size near the pump. This is to give a rapid and uniform distribution of the solution. At the point where the discharge fitting enters the bench, it is best to countersink the fitting by cutting part way through the bottom of the bench board in order to get the discharge opening flush with the bottom of the bench and so allow complete drainage.

WATERPROOFING THE BENCHES

We now come to the waterproofing of the benches. Of the several methods tried, the one found to be *best* and *cheapest* is ordinary asphalt roofer's felt and hot Korite.* By actual test, we also found it cheaper to have a regular roofer do the work, as he has the proper equipment and knows exactly how to do it.

First cut strips of felt 12 inches wide and fold them in the middle so that they will cover the full width of the side and lap over 6 inches on the bottom of the bench. Cut away this paper at the reinforcing cleats to make a clean joint. Next cut enough squares 6 inches by 6 inches to use on the lapped cleats of the side boards. Apply these squares as shown by first mopping the cleat and the adjacent 3 or 4 inches with hot Korite and pressing one of these squares firmly against the side so that it covers the end of the cleat and laps over 2 or 3 inches on both the side board and the cleat. After all such cleats are prepared in this way, mop the side board and 6 inches of the bottom with hot Korite, and lay on the 12-inch folded strip previously cut so that it covers the side of the bench and laps 6 inches over the bottom. After the sides are treated in this way, mop the entire bottom of the bench with hot Korite, and cover this with a continuous layer of the felt. Wherever joints are necessary, always allow at least 3 to 4 inches

* Korite is manufactured by the Standard Oil of Indiana, Home Office, Chicago, Illinois.

lap, and be sure that these seams are thoroughly mopped with Korite. Now give entire bottom and sides a heavy coat of Korite, taking particular care to see that all joints, cleats, and corners are watertight, as these are the most likely places for leaks to occur. (Although we specify Korite No. 1, which is a Standard Oil product, no doubt equally good products of this same type are made by other companies. CAUTION: Be sure to avoid coal-tar compounds.)

It is necessary to use an inverted trough of some kind down the length of the bench to get uniform rapid distribution of the nutrient. We have tried several methods, and again the *best* way was the *cheapest*. Rip a 6-inch board down the middle 2½ inches by 3½ inches, and nail the two pieces together to form a V trough. See Fig. 9. Mop this with hot Korite on all sides. Then invert this trough over the discharge opening. Laid loosely on the bench, it serves merely to give free distribution of the nutrient throughout the entire bench area. The

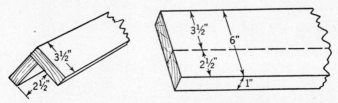

FIG. 9. This shows the method of making the inverted V trough which after being completely coated with Korite is placed lengthwise down the center of the bench to give even distribution of the nutrient solution and at the same time prevent cinders and dirt from getting into the distributing system.

solution flows under the edges, but the cinders or gravel are prevented from getting back into the system. As stated before, if the benches are in good shape and can be properly leveled without tearing them down and rebuilding, all you need do is caulk them with oakum, cleat and brace them for strength, and then proceed to waterproof them with building paper and Korite as above. See Fig. 10. This will save a great deal of expense, and for that reason it may be well to select a house that is in excellent condition unless the one you already have needs the benches rebuilt. If you are going to build entirely new benches from new materials, we strongly urge you to build concrete benches as they will last indefinitely. The initial cost will be a little more, but the waterproofing will be much cheaper as only two good coats of asphalt emulsion are needed instead of the building paper and Korite combination. As the building of concrete benches presents a

Fig. 10. Actual bench as constructed according to our specifications. Note heavy wire bracing the side of the bench, strengthening cleat at the joint in the side boards, and tin collar near center of bench which is placed around purlin post as shown at left. Purlin posts must be painted with Korite as shown, wide cracks covered with tin and narrow cracks stuffed with oakum.

number of problems for the amateur, we recommend turning the job over to an expert. Among those who do an excellent job are the Winandy Greenhouse Construction Company, of Richmond, Indiana. You may also be interested in reading the latest bulletin on bench design written by R. B. Farnham and W. C. Kreuger, of the New Jersey Experiment Station. It may be had on request.

Remember that, in running pipe and fittings, all parts should be black iron, for the zinc galvanizing contaminates the solution. Proper valves should be used in the piping so that any house can be operated independently and so that any bench may be shut off or drained without shutting down the entire installation. This is important when repairs or other work is necessary. Always use large enough pipe to give a a good free gravity flow back to the tank. If you use a centrifugal pump, no return line is needed, since as soon as the pump stops the solution immediately begins to drain back into the tank. *Be sure* to place the pump below the high-water level of the nutrient tank so that it will not lose its prime.

We want to call attention now to a much simpler installation for the person who wishes to experiment with nutrients on a small scale. This simple installation is thoroughly practical but it is not entirely automatic, since the motor, pump, and time switch are omitted. It is designed for home use or for the man who wants to prove to himself that what we say about nutrient culture is true, before he invests any great amount of money in permanent equipment. Complete details are presented in Chapter IV.

MECHANICAL EQUIPMENT

The mechanical equipment such as motors, pumps, and automatic electrical controls is described in detail in the following pages. It is well to bear in mind that in a commercial installation where it is necessary to have continuous carefree operation it is important to install the very best equipment. In specifying the size and type of pump, we must take into consideration the job to be done. The benches should be filled with the nutrient solution in 30 to 40 minutes of pump operation. The size of pump and motor needed is determined by the number of gallons of solution to be pumped, the height to which it is pumped, the amount of friction in the pipe, and the time allowed for pumping the solution into the benches. In the ordinary installation the tank is about 5 feet deep and it is about 5 feet more to the top of the benches. If the tank to be pumped contains 3,000 gallons of solution, we need a pump and motor that will pump that amount in 30 minutes against a 10-foot head. That is equivalent to pumping 6,000 gallons per hour or 100 gallons per minute against a 10-foot head. The pump should have a cast-iron impeller and a stainless-steel shaft. Avoid zinc-coated pumps or pipes. A motor of adequate size is usually directly connected to the pump, and the whole may be purchased from any reliable pump company. See Fig. 11, showing a suitable pump.

FIG. 11. A typical direct-connected motor-driven centrifugal pump such as is used to force the solution from the tank to the benches.

Yeomans Brothers Company, 1433 Dayton Street, Chicago, Illinois; Fairbanks-Morse Company, Michigan Avenue, Chicago, Illinois; American Well Works, Aurora, Illinois; and Deming Pump Company, Salem, Ohio, are among the dependable manufacturers of such equipment.

You will need a reliable electrical time switch with a 24-hour dial, and at least three pairs of operating levers. This allows three "on" and "off" periods each day, and we have found that number of feedings to be sufficient. A desirable period between "on" and "off" is 30 minutes, and the period between "off" and "on" is 2½ hours or longer. This will account for three feedings during the daylight hours. A satisfactory switch with three operating periods may be purchased from the Sangamo Electric Company, Springfield, Illinois. A more flexible switch with many more operating periods available can be purchased from the General Electric Company. See Fig. 12. Either company makes

FIG. 12. View showing operating dial of the General Electric Time Switch. Although only two operating levers are shown several more are furnished. Such a switch controls all watering and feeding.

thoroughly reliable equipment. Automatic time switches of this sort save much time and the trouble of watching the pumps and turning them on and off at each feeding. It makes the watering and feeding absolutely automatic. However, some prefer to do this by hand.

If your installation is of such size that you operate several houses, tanks, and pumps from one time switch, you will need an automatic overload relay. If the installation is properly designed and installed this relay seldom operates, but, in case of an unexpected overload of the circuits, it will throw out, thus shutting off the current and saving costly repairs to the motors or time switch. A good type of relay for this purpose may be purchased from the Cutler Hammer Company, 116 North Green Street, Chicago. By means of this overload relay, a number of pumps can be run off the same time switch. This gives an economical installation, saves wiring costs, and is very satisfactory. All the motors and pumps must be operated at the same time, but this is not a disadvantage. Each pump or motor should have an individual hand switch at the pump pit. This enables each pump to be cut off at any time without disturbing the operation of the rest of the system. These hand switches should be of the outside type, waterproof, and thoroughly insulated, as there is a great deal of water and moisture at all times and the danger of serious electrical shock must be avoided by using only approved equipment, in which the shock hazard is minimized. All wiring should be carried in conduit and run where it will not be exposed to excessive water or moisture.

We recommend that you present your problem to the representative of a reliable pump company, who will be glad to give you specifications and quote prices on the proper size of pump, motor, and piping. You may find it cheaper in the long run to use large pipe in your runs to the benches, which will enable you to use a smaller pump and motor and thus result in a saving of electricity every month. We also suggest that, if you are considering growing several crops requiring different solutions, you can secure greater flexibility by having two small pumps directly connected to one motor and so pump two different solutions from adjacent tanks with one installation. If you have just one pump connecting two adjacent tanks, you must use the same solution in both tanks.

Average Cost of Converting

The cost of making such changes varies with the locality and also depends on labor costs and transportation charges. The following list will give you an approximate cost of installing high-grade equipment in two typical houses 30 feet by 200 feet:

Motor-driven pump (2½-in. pump, 1½-hp. motor).............. $95.00
Valves, fittings, and pipe ($75 per house)........................ 150.00
Waterproofing wooden benches ($125 per house)................ 250.00
6000-gal.-capacity tank (materials and labor) 75.00
Time switch (only one for any number of houses).............. 20.00
Automatic overload relay.. 18.00
Miscellaneous electrical equipment 10.00

$618.00

A 3,000-gallon tank (approximately 12,000 liters) will take care of one house with five benches 3½ feet by 200 feet. The cost per house is slightly more than shown if only one house at a time is so equipped. A definite saving is effected by converting houses in pairs, as shown, since much of the equipment can be purchased in larger sizes and only one installation cost is involved. In addition to the above, you will need an accurate solution testing kit (approximate cost $10 to $20) and a sensitive balance for weighing the salts that make up the solution formula (approximate cost $45 to $75, depending upon the capacity of the balance). These items are mentioned specifically in the chapter on nutrient-solution formulas. Of course, only one testing kit and one balance are required, regardless of the size of your installation; therefore this cost need be figured only once. This is true also of the time switch and overload relay, as any number of pumps can be operated from one set.

After the benches have been rebuilt and waterproofed, the tank constructed, and the electrical equipment installed, it is time to prepare the benches for planting. Several factors govern the selection of the material used in the benches to support the root system. Cost, availability, and chemical characteristics of the material are important.

Filling the Benches

Some crops require an alkaline soil or solution. For them, limestone gravel may be used. This type of bench fill is readily available in the Middle West and is suitable for such crops as sweet peas. Those crops which require a high acidity should have a gravel practically free from lime such as is found in parts of Ohio and Wisconsin. Ohio gravel is white and contains no iron; Wisconsin gravel is dark and contains iron, but whether in an available form and in sufficient quantities as required by roses, we cannot say as we have not used it.*

* Of course, there are many sources of suitable gravel, and we suggest that you investigate and test your local supply before securing gravels from a distance.

Any gravel used should be about ⅜ to ¼ inch in size. This affords a good protection for the roots, allows plenty of aeration, and is neither too fine nor too coarse. Gravel probably is a permanent medium in which to grow plants. Biekart and Connors of New Jersey report that they have used the same sand for six years without any apparent injury to the plants, and they believe that it can be used for many more years.

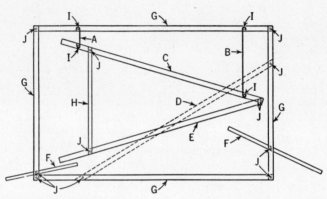

Fig. 13. Method of making a simple double screen for preparing cinders. Diagram shows relative position of various members. Use sound 2 by 6's and make a cubical framework by bolting the parts together as shown. It should be about 10 feet long, 6 feet high, and 4 feet wide. Angular braces should be used on all sides and ends as indicated to keep it steady. Inside this framework mount two 8-foot screens at about the angle shown, using short hooks at the high end and longer hooks at the low end. The coarse screen on top should be about 1-inch mesh, and the fine screen on the bottom should be ¼-inch mesh. Provide a shute at each end of the machine to carry the cinders into piles at either end. Throw the regular cinders onto the top screen; rock the screens back and forth so that the coarse cinders will fall in a pile at one end; the fine material will fall in the center and the usable size will discharge at the other end.

A—Short hooks. B—Long hooks. C—Coarse screen. D—Angular brace. E—Fine screen. F—Shutes. G—Cubical frame. H—Brace for screens. I—Rods to hold hooks. J—Bolts to hold frame rigid.

We have found that ordinary cinders are highly satisfactory and economical for bench fill, but they must be properly prepared. They need to be screened so as to get uniform, medium-sized pieces. This is not difficult, and we illustrate a simple screen that will be entirely satisfactory and is easily constructed. The cinders also need to be leached to free them of excess sulfur and gases, but this can be done after they are put in the benches. We have not found it necessary to allow them to leach and weather outside for a year as some have recommended. Of course, if cinders are available that have weathered for some time, their preparation in the bench will probably be simplified.

For the purpose of getting only those cinders of proper size, we suggest that you make the simple double screen as shown. See Fig. 13. By throwing the cinders onto the top screen, the large pieces fall off one end, the medium and fine pieces fall through onto the lower screen, where the too fine particles fall through to the ground and the usable sizes fall off into a pile opposite the large pieces. From this pile, the usable cinders can be wheeled directly into the benches. CAUTION: If you will cover the bottom of the benches with a little water, the cinders can be wheeled in just as soil is handled and the asphalt waterproofing of the benches will not be injured.

The top screen should have about 1-inch mesh and the bottom screen a ⅛-inch mesh. If these screens are mounted in a frame and hung on pipe as shown in the sketch, they can be rocked back and forth to facilitate screen'ng the material.*

After the benches are filled level with the screened cinders, they should be flooded with clear water and allowed to stand for two days. This water can be applied with a hose, but be sure to close the valve at the end of the bench so that the water will not drain out of the bench into the nutrient tank. At the end of two days drain off this water and refill with fresh water, allowing it to stand in the benches another two days. Then drain again and refill with fresh water, but this time add enough concentrated sulfuric acid to bring the acidity down to about pH 3 and allow this to stand for three or four days. (It usually requires about 1 gallon of acid for each bench 3½ feet by 100 feet.) However, the acidity should be tested to be sure. (See Chapter 10, "Testing Nutrient Solutions.") Although we have used coal from many sources our cinders have always been alkaline in reaction. Others have reported that their cinders were acid in reaction, in which case a strong solution of lye is added, instead of the sulfuric acid, to bring the acidity to pH 6 or 7. It is important to treat the cinders with acid or lye before any planting is done because, after the plants are put in the bench, the acid or lye can be added only in such small quantities, for fear of injuring the roots, that it may take months of constant attention to bring the pH to the proper point.

The term pH of a solution refers to the relative acidity or alka-

---

* It may be possible for you to rent from your local gravel dealer a regular motor-driven gravel screener which will enable you to screen your cinders quickly and at a lower cost. See Fig. 14.

FIG. 14. A motor-driven screener which may sometimes be rented and will do a quicker job and possibly at less cost. Gravel dealers and coal dealers have such machines.

linity of the solution and is explained in greater detail in Chapter 5, "Chemistry and Mathematics of Nutrient Solutions." The method of testing the pH of cinders is explained in Chapter 10. Using an ordinary glass of cinders, fill it with distilled water, allow it to stand 2 or 3 hours, and then test this liquid to determine whether the cinders are acid or alkaline.

In the next chapter, we present some modifications of the system just described. This equipment is not experimental but has been thoroughly tried and has grown highly satisfactory crops. It is intended for the skeptical or timid individual or those lacking the funds to invest in the automatic devices mentioned above.

Chapter IV

SMALL-SCALE NUTRIENT EQUIPMENT

Some who are seriously interested in growing plants in nutrient solutions may want to experiment for various reasons on a small scale before investing money in the automatic equipment described for large commercial installations. For those who want a simple inexpensive method we give the details of a few systems that have been used and are thoroughly practicable. Reference to the diagrams will show exactly how these arrangements are set up.

Waterproof Box Method

Waterproof containers or boxes will be needed. They may be of any convenient size and need not be more than 6 inches in depth for any average crop. If the first method we suggest is adopted we caution you not to make the boxes too large or the solution buckets will be too heavy to handle conveniently. The boxes in which the plants grow may be made of almost any material. If they are to be used in the home they can be built of much better lumber for appearance sake; otherwise any rough lumber is adequate, waterproofed with building paper and Korite in the same manner as recommended for greenhouse benches in Chapter III. A suitable size is 4 feet long and 10 inches wide. Such a box would have a volume of approximately 45 liters and would require a container for the nutrient solution about one-third this capacity or 15 liters. A galvanized or enameled 4-gallon pail (16 quarts) would serve nicely as the solution container. If a galvanized pail is used care must be taken to cover all metal parts that might come in contact with the solution, with Korite, or with an asphalt emulsion. The box has a metal spout attached to it, and a metal spout is soldered to the pail. A flexible hose about 3 feet long connects these two spouts. By hanging the bucket on a hook above the box the solution runs by gravity into the gravel, where it is allowed to remain for about 30 minutes. The bucket is then placed on a hook below the level of the box, and the solution drains from the gravel into the pail. This process is repeated three times daily at 3-hour intervals. See Fig. 15.

A box of this size will hold four plants of medium growth such as roses, gardenias, callas, or tomatoes. If smaller plants are used, more may be grown. In a greenhouse, these boxes may be placed in any convenient location; in the home, a bright sunny location must be chosen. Should you prefer to use the ordinary fernery or window-box containing a metal liner, you must cover the inside of the liner thor-

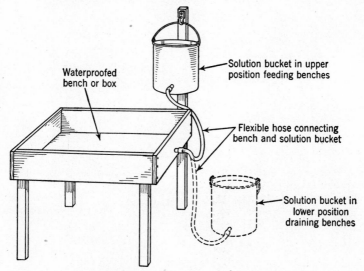

Turner's Original Experimental Method (Hand Operated)

FIG. 15. Diagram of small hand-operated method of feeding nutrient solutions. This method was used successfully for a year and is thoroughly practical. Can be used with individual boxes or with sections of a bench.

oughly with Korite or an asphalt emulsion so that no metal comes in contact with the solution.

When the box and solution bucket are ready, the box should be filled with gravel low in calcium, about ¼-inch in diameter.

SECTIONAL BENCH METHOD

If you wish to use a portion of your regular greenhouse bench, you can divide it into sections 10 or 12 inches wide, waterproof it as before, and provide a solution-pail for each section. In this way several different crops and several different solutions may be used, as each section is a separate unit.

Another method that has been employed at the University of Illinois provides automatic control but enables the grower to use several solutions independently and grow several different crops. This system requires a time switch, a motor-driven air compressor, and several airtight solution-containers. These solution-containers may be 5-gallon jugs or airtight drums. They are connected to a compressed-air line as shown in the diagram. See Fig. 16. In this system the compressor builds up the air pressure in the solution-containers and forces the solution up into the benches or boxes. The compressor stops, the pressure is released, and the solution returns to the container. The principal advantage of this system over that described in our com-

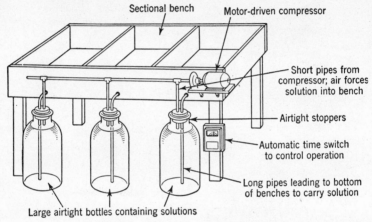

FIG. 16. Diagram of automatic system of feeding nutrient solutions to several boxes or bench sections using only one pump. Several different solutions may be used simultaneously if desired.

mercial installation is that it is adaptable to smaller units and a multiplicity of solutions and crops. This involves buying some automatic equipment, but most of it can be used when you convert larger portions of your range as you gain confidence in this method of growing.

Whether the feeding is done by mechanical means or by hand, it must be done regularly. One has no right to expect satisfactory results if the process is neglected in any way. The solution must be kept in the proper proportion and at the correct level. A great deal of water is lost by evaporation and must be replaced. You should mark the exact level at which the solution should be maintained on the solution-container and see that it is kept at that point. Acidity should be checked and held at the point recommended for the crop being grown.

If you are using small quantities of solution, it will no doubt be much simpler to change the solutions regularly each week, discarding the old and putting in fresh solution to replace the depleted elements. In this way the acidity is not likely to change if you adjusted it properly when the solution was first made up.

Solutions are made in the same manner, and the calculations as to amount of salts to use are made in the same way, as for large installations. The fertilizer compounds are the same. Care must be exercised to have the weights of the salts exact because in small quantities an error of 1 gram is equivalent to an error of 1,000 grams in a large tank. If you do not have a highly accurate balance, no doubt your druggist will weigh your salts for you. Since you will need a really accurate balance if you ultimately use nutrients on a large scale it would be wise to buy one now and become accustomed to using it.

Making Stock Solution

To eliminate mixing small quantities of solution at weekly intervals, the solution can be made up in quantities of 100-200 gallons and stored in barrels or drums. Such a stock solution can be made up in a concentrated form and simply diluted properly when used in the boxes. If you do make up a concentrated solution, be sure to mark it so that you will know the exact amount of water to add when you change your solution. We advise making the solution in these larger amounts as it saves time and lessens the possibility of errors in weighing and mixing. Although in Chapters VI and VII we give the exact details of mixing and calculating the amount of salts required by a formula, we want to mention here the method of making a stock solution for small installations. Suppose that you have five boxes of the size we described. Each box requires about 15 liters of solution, which is approximately 4 gallons. You will find that some of the formulas are given on the basis of so many grams of the salt per 100 gallons of solution. Suppose that your calculations show that you need 60 grams of ammonium sulfate to make 100 gallons of solution. If you dissolve 120 grams of ammonium sulfate in 50 gallons of water you will have four times as concentrated a solution as the formula calls for.*
This 50 gallons can be stored in a 50-gallon barrel and used as needed to replenish your nutrients weekly. If you were using a stock solution of this concentration you would take 1 gallon of the stock solution and

---

* To this same 50 gallons add proportionate amounts of the other salts called for in the formula you are using.

3 gallons of pure water for each unit of your installation. In this way by weighing and mixing the stock solution only once you have enough solution to recharge your unit containers ten times.

If you grow your plants in nutrients only during the normal outside growing season, May 15 to September 15, no adjustment in the proportion of nitrogen and potassium need be made during the season. The same solution, a fresh supply being provided each week, would no doubt be satisfactory. However, if you are going to grow your crop through the winter season when the length of the day and the intensity of the light are constantly changing, it will be necessary to regulate the amount of nitrogen and potassium to correspond with these changing light conditions. By studying the chapter on nutrient solutions you will notice that the potassium must be increased during the short dark days, and that the nitrogen must be increased during the longer sunny days.

SUGGESTED ACIDITY FOR VARIOUS CROPS

Just as we emphasize the necessity for watching the acidity of the solution in a large commercial installation, so it is necessary to watch it in a small experimental plot. If you make up a quantity of stock solution and change it weekly you will not need to check this point except at the time of making up your solution as the acidity will not change in the drum or barrel but will remain constant. Most greenhouse plants prefer an acidity of pH 5-6. Below we list a number of plants and the acidity that seems to be best for them. If you grow several kinds, be sure that those which require the same acidity are grown together.

ACIDITY REQUIRED

pH 4-5	pH 5-6	pH 6-7	
Ageratum	Bean (Lima)	Alyssum	Columbine
Azalea	Candytuft	Anemone	Coreopsis
Lily-of-the-valley	Lupin	Aster	Gaillardia
Potatoes	Watermelon	Bean (string)	Nasturtium
Rhododendron	Calla lilies	Begonia	Sweet peas
Speedwell	Bermuda lilies	Calendula	Petunias
Gardenia	Snapdragons	Cantaloupe	Phlox
		Chrysanthemums	Tomatoes

In determining the concentration of the nutrient solution, we speak of so many parts per million (ppm.) of the desired element in the solution. Ordinarily for most summer crops a solution containing 450 ppm. of nitrogen, 100 ppm. of potassium, 70 ppm. of phosphorus,

PLATE I

This installation was constructed on an outside roof terrace by an amateur, who applied the information and directions exactly as given herein. The bench material was purchased locally, the tank and motor were from a discarded washer, and the water-circulating pump was from an automobile. The solution tank was coated inside with asphalt emulsion. To avoid dilution of the solution during heavy rains, an extra valve was provided to carry off the water that fell in the bench during a storm. The bench was 14 feet by 2 feet. It was planted with tomatoes, potatoes, asters, petunias, scabiosa, zinnias, marigolds, calendulas, and balsam—about 65 plants in all. This miscellaneous crop thrived in the same solution.

and 60 ppm. of magnesium would be correct with the acidity at the proper point as shown in the above table.

VISIBLE DEFICIENCY SYMPTOMS

Iron must be fed occasionally, as this element is important for most crops and prevents chlorosis. Iron chlorosis can be noted easily as it causes a spotting of the leaf. The veins remain green and the interveinal surfaces become yellow.

A deficiency of nitrogen may be noted by lack of growth, hardness of wood, and a yellowing of the foliage. In this case the leaves are not spotted but are of a uniform pale color.

A deficiency of potash would show up by a rank weak growth, and an excess of potash would show up by a hard stunted growth.

If you adopt the method of changing the solutions weekly, it will not be necessary to test them, as the depleted salts will be replaced by the new solution.

Care should be used in studying the chapter on deficiency symptoms. In this method we are eliminating much of the testing procedure which we recommend for the large commercial installation. We do this only to save the cost of the testing equipment. We urge you, if you can see your way to do so, to buy the same testing equipment and a set of fine balances, and to carry on even your small experiments in the same fine detail as though you were operating on a large scale. It is only in that way that you can learn and prove to yourself the true value of this method of growing. If you do not take advantage of all the tests and safeguards that are available, you will still be able to grow a good crop, probably as good a crop as you would grow in soil using the usual hit-or-miss methods that sometimes prevail; but if you will follow the methods that have been proven you will undoubtedly become enthusiastic about this "new" cultural method.

We have not gone into the subject of growing in tanks outdoors although the principles laid down in this book are readily applicable to such culture. Several good bulletins are available which tell how to construct tanks for outdoor culture, and the same basic formulas and methods apply to that as to indoor culture. You are, of course, limited in your growing season to the period of mild weather prevailing in your locality. You will find that you can probably grow a larger crop and possibly mature it earlier using nutrient solutions than you can in regular soil culture.

Chapter V

CHEMISTRY AND MATHEMATICS OF NUTRIENT SOLUTIONS

Most growers of flowers or vegetables have at least some familiarity with chemistry. They know the composition of most of the fertilizers which they use. It is not necessary that they know all the chemical reactions involved in nutrient culture, but a very brief and simple discussion of chemistry will enable them to understand better just what takes place.

CHEMICAL DEFINITIONS

As you probably know, all matter in the world is composed of various combinations of different substances. In the science of chemistry the breaking up of these substances into their basic parts gives what are known to us as the elements. In other words, an element is a substance that cannot be broken up into other substances. Some of the common elements are iron, sulfur, oxygen, calcium, and nitrogen.

An element cannot be broken up into other substances; but two or more elements can be united to form a new substance. These combinations are called compounds. Examples of compounds are salt (sodium chloride, $NaCl$), baking soda (sodium bicarbonate, $NaHCO_3$), water (H_2O), epsom salts (magnesium sulfate, $MgSO_4$). Although there are about ninety-two known elements, we are concerned with only fourteen of them, as they are the ones which growing plants require.

Each element has a definite name and is commonly represented by a symbol which is an abbreviation of either its common or Latin name.

At this point we need two definitions to explain some of the chemical reactions which we employ and calculations which we make in using nutrients. A *molecule* is the smallest unit quantity of matter that can exist by itself and retain all the properties of the original substance. An *atom* is the smallest unit quantity of an element that can enter into chemical combination.

Fig. 17. King Cardinal carnations grown continuously through two years. Note walk built on top edge of bench in order to cut crop. This resulted in an excellent summer crop and eliminated the usual loss due to making cuttings.

FIG. 18. Two-year-old Briarcliff roses grown in nutrients. Many of these roses had flowers on stems so long that a man standing on the top edge of the bench could not reach them. These results were obtained without extra pinching.

The atoms of each chemical element have definite and characteristic weights. In order to provide a uniform basis for designating these atomic weights, the hydrogen atom, which is the lightest, is given the rating of one (1), and all other atomic weights are shown as a certain number of times heavier than hydrogen. For example: oxygen (O) is given an atomic weight of 16 since it is sixteen times heavier than hydrogen, and potassium (K) is given an atomic weight of 39 since it is thirty-nine times heavier than hydrogen. The reason for stressing these atomic weights is that in making up our nutrient solutions we use these various weights to give a uniform and definite formula.

ESSENTIAL ELEMENTS

The table below shows the fourteen elements with which we work in nutrient culture. Listed beside each element are the chemical symbol by which the element is ordinarily designated and the approximate atomic weight.

FOURTEEN ELEMENTS USED IN NUTRIENT CULTURE

Element	Symbol	Approximate Atomic Weights	Element	Symbol	Approximate Atomic Weights
Boron	B	11	Manganese	Mn	55
Calcium	Ca	40	Nitrogen	N	14
Carbon	C	12	Oxygen	O	16
Copper (cuprum)	Cu	64	Phosphorus	P	31
Hydrogen	H	1	Potassium (kalium)	K	39
Iron (ferrum)	Fe	56	Sulfur	S	32
Magnesium	Mg	24	Zinc	Zn	65

Although these fourteen elements are the important ones from our standpoint, some of the other elements will be found in the chemicals which we use in our solutions. These others are not needed, and we will consider them only as unimportant impurities. It is much more economical to use fertilizer-grade chemicals which contain such impurities than to buy absolutely pure chemicals. In our solutions we use two classes of chemicals: major elements, which are used in large quantities; and minor elements, which are used in very small quantities. By using the fertilizer grade of chemicals we frequently do not have to add the minor elements because they are present as impurities and in sufficient quantities for our purpose. Certain elements are distinctly detrimental to plant growth and should be carefully avoided if the analysis of the fertilizer shows enough of this toxic element to harm the growing plant.

Compounds are derived by the union of one or more elements. Also elements can be divided into their smaller parts, called either molecules or atoms.* It is these small atoms which unite when a chemical reaction takes place. Water is a compound; it is composed of two atoms hydrogen (H) to one atom oxygen (O). The formula is H_2O. Nitric acid is composed of one atom hydrogen, one atom nitrogen (N), and three atoms oxygen. The formula is HNO_3. Sulfuric acid is composed of two atoms hydrogen, one atom sulfur (S), and four atoms oxygen. The formula is H_2SO_4. Just as the atoms of each of these elements have a definite atomic weight, so the molecules of these compounds have a definite molecular weight which is equal to the combined atomic weights of the elements composing the compound.

DETERMINING MOLECULAR WEIGHT

As an example, suppose that we wish to find the molecular weight of nitric acid, HNO_3:

ELEMENT: H + N + O + O + O = HNO_3 (Get the atomic weight from the
ATOMIC   table of atomic weights.)
WEIGHT: 1 + 14 + 16 + 16 + 16 = 63, or the molecular weight of nitric acid;

or to find the molecular weight of epsom salts, $MgSO_4$:

ELEMENT: Mg + S + O + O + O + O = $MgSO_4$
ATOMIC
WEIGHT: 24 + 32 + 16 + 16 + 16 + 16 = 120 or the molecular weight of $MgSO_4$.

As these various elements, hydrogen (H), nitrogen (N), and oxygen (O), can be combined to form nitric acid (HNO_3), so nitric acid can be broken up into its elements, hydrogen, nitrogen, and oxygen. This breaking up of chemical compounds occurs in growing plants and is the method by which the plant extracts the elements it needs for proper growth.

FERTILIZER SALTS

The fertilizing compounds that we use in nutrient solutions are usually composed of various "salts." A salt is a compound formed by

---

* Ordinarily elements divide into atoms but occasionally they divide naturally into molecules made up of two or more atoms. An example is hydrogen gas (H_2) consisting of two atoms of hydrogen forming one molecule of hydrogen.

the replacement of the hydrogen element in an acid by a metallic element, thus:

Nitric acid + Sodium hydroxide (lye) → Sodium nitrate + Water
$$HNO_3 \; + \qquad NaOH \qquad \rightarrow \qquad NaNO_3 \quad + \; H_2O$$

In this reaction, sodium nitrate is formed, and this is one of the salts that can be used in nutrient solutions. However, we do not have to combine these chemicals in this fashion as nature has done the work for us and we get sodium nitrate as a natural salt from mines. (It might be well to note that the salt formed takes its name from the acid used to make it. Thus nitric acid forms nitrates, sulfuric acid forms sulfates, and phosphoric acid forms phosphates.)

Not all salts are soluble in water, but we are concerned only with those that are. In making up our formulas, we must have a standard of measuring the amount of each salt or other substance in the solution so that we will know its concentration. For this purpose the "molar" solution was devised. A molar solution means a molecular-weight solution. A molar solution is made by dissolving, in water, the molecular weight in grams of the compound used and then diluting this solution to 1 liter. As explained before, the molecular weight is the combined atomic weights of the elements composing the compound. As a simple example: to make a molar solution of pure potassium nitrate (KNO_3) we find the molecular weight just as before:

$$KNO_3 = K + N + O + O + O$$
$$39 + 14 + 16 + 16 + 16 = 101, \text{ the molecular weight.}$$

Therefore if we dissolve 101 grams of pure potassium nitrate in a small amount of water and then add enough water to make 1 liter of solution, we have a molar solution of potassium nitrate. This solution is too strong to use with growing plants, so we dilute the molar solution and obtain just 1/1,000 the concentration; this is called a "millimole" solution (so named from the Latin prefix "milli" meaning one-thousandth). In other words, we dissolve this same molecular weight (101 grams) in water and dilute to 1,000 liters. Since many of the compounds we use in making our nutrient solutions are not pure, we must make an additional calculation as explained in Chapter VI.

RELATIVE ACIDITY OR pH

Since it has been found that the acidity or alkalinity of our nutrient solution has a great bearing on the results obtained, it will be well to explain how this acidity is expressed and what it means. Scientists have learned that certain groups of elements have a great tendency to stay together and are not readily separated. In the case of nitric acid (HNO_3) it is possible to separate the hydrogen (H), the nitrogen (N), and the oxygen (O), but ordinarily this group of elements divides in a different way thus: the hydrogen (H) separates and the nitrate group (NO_3) stays together and unites as a unit. Such a group of atoms that have an "affinity" for each other is called a "radical." Thus we have the nitrate radical (NO_3), the sulfate radical (SO_4), the phosphate radical (PO_4), and many others. These are also called acid radicals because they appear in the acid compounds.

Another group, quite similar to the acid radical, is called the hydroxyl radical. This radical is composed of one atom of oxygen (O) and one atom of hydrogen (H) united in this way (OH). When this radical unites with a metal we have an alkaline substance such as sodium hydroxide (NaOH), which is ordinary lye. Hydroxides are alkaline in reaction and neutralize acids. If our nutrient solution becomes acid we can correct it by adding an alkaline substance, or if it becomes alkaline we can correct it by adding an acid. As mentioned before, the acidity or alkalinity of our nutrient solution is quite important. The term used to describe the degree of acidity or alkalinity is the pH of the solution. This refers to the relative acidity or alkalinity of the solution. The scale runs from pH 0 to pH 14. Solutions more acid than pH 4 or more alkaline than pH 9 usually are not suitable for crop production. A solution with a pH of 7 is neutral; a solution below pH 7 is acid, and one above pH 7 is alkaline. Most plants thrive best in a slightly acid solution such as pH 5 to 6. (A definite method of testing the pH of a solution will be given later.)

It is well to remember that some of the elements used in our nutrient solutions are not assimilated by the plant but function by making some other element more readily available or by reducing the toxicity of some substance. Such a chemical that does not enter directly into the chemical reaction but aids in the reaction without itself changing is called a catalytic agent.[*]

An understanding of the foregoing principles of chemistry is necessary to success with nutrient culture. If you want to do more research work and experimentation, you will need a thorough knowledge of chemistry, but anyone who masters the simple facts outlined in this chapter will be able to grow excellent crops by the nutrient-culture

---

[*] All elements *purposely* added to the present-day nutrient solution are used functionally by the plant. Some of the minor elements which occur as impurities in the fertilizer grade of salts used may act as catalytic agents.

method. The practical application of these principles will be indicated in detail in later chapters.

Almost always things understood mean the difference between success and failure. The process of making up the various solutions used in nutrient culture is neither complicated nor mysterious, but is greatly simplified by using the metric system of weights and measures. A working knowledge of this method of calculating will not only enable you to ascertain accurately the various concentrations of the solutions but will also give you the key to a proper understanding of the valuable technical bulletins brought out from time to time by the agricultural experiment stations as new developments arise.

Metric System

The following is a brief description of the metric system and terminology. The *meter* is the basic unit of length of the metric system; it corresponds approximately to the English yard. (One meter equals 39.37 inches.) Larger units or multiples are designated by prefixing certain Greek words to the basic word "meter." Thus "Deka" means ten—Dekameter (Dm.) equals 10 meters; "Hekta" means hundred—Hektameter (Hm.) equals 100 meters; "Kilo" means thousand—Kilometer (Km.) equals 1,000 meters. In like fashion, smaller units or submultiples are designated by prefixing certain Latin words to the basic word "meter." Thus "deci" means tenth—decimeter (dm.) equals $\frac{1}{10}$ of a meter; "centi" means hundredth—centimeter (cm.) equals $\frac{1}{100}$ of a meter; "milli" means thousandth—millimeter (mm.) equals $\frac{1}{1,000}$ of a meter. (Notice that in the abbreviations the larger units or multiples are capitalized while the smaller units or submultiples begin with a small letter.) These same Greek and Latin prefixes are used to designate multiples and submultiples when added to the unit of weight (the gram—g.) or the unit of capacity (the liter—l.), and they have the same relative meaning.

The simplicity of the metric system, because it is a decimal system, the various units of length, weight, and capacity being interrelated decimally, recommends it for universal use as it simplifies all calculations.

The metric unit of weight is the gram (g.), which is the weight of 1 cubic centimeter of water at 4 degrees centigrade. (Water at this temperature has its greatest density.) From this you can see how readily the weight of a given volume of water may be determined—simply calculate the volume in cubic centimeters (cc.), and you immediately also have the weight in grams because each cubic centimeter weighs 1 gram.

The metric unit of capacity is the liter (l.). One liter equals 1,000 cc. (The English equivalent "quart" is slightly smaller—1 liter equals 1.0567 quarts.) The interrelation of the liter and cubic centimeters shows how readily metric units of length may be converted into volume, weight, and capacity. The length times the width times the depth of a tank when expressed in cubic centimeters, divided by 1,000, gives the volume of the tank in liters. In determining the concentration of our nutrient solutions we speak of so many parts per million. An important thing to remember is that 1 milligram of a substance dissolved in 1 liter of water gives 1 part per million (1 ppm.) of that substance in the water (or 1 gram in 1,000 liters equals 1 ppm.).

METRIC TABLE OF LENGTH

(Km.)	One Kilometer equals...........	1,000.	meters
(Hm.)	One Hektometer equals.........	100.	meters
(Dm.)	One Dekameter equals..........	10.	meters
(m.)	One *meter* equals..............	1.	meter, or 39.37 inches or 100 cm. or 1,000 mm.
(dm.)	One decimeter equals...........	0.1	meter
(cm.)	One centimeter equals..........	0.01	meter
(mm.)	One millimeter equals...........	0.001	meter

(One inch = 2.54 cm.)

METRIC TABLE OF WEIGHT

(Kg.)	One Kilogram equals............	1,000.	grams
(Hg.)	One Hektogram equals.........	100.	grams
(Dg.)	One Dekagram equals..........	10.	grams
(g.)	One *gram* equals..............	1.	gram, or weight of 1 cc. water or 1,000 mg.
(dg.)	One decigram equals............	0.1	gram
(cg.)	One centigram equals..........	0.01	gram
(mg.)	One milligram equals...........	0.001	gram

(1 Kilogram (Kg.) = 2.204 lb.)

METRIC TABLE OF CAPACITY

(Kl.)	One Kiloliter equals.............	1,000.	liters	1,000,000 cc.
(Hl.)	One Hektoliter equals...........	100.	liters	100,000 cc.
(Dl.)	One Dekaliter equals...........	10.	liters	10,000 cc.
(l.)	One *liter* equals................	1.	liter or	1,000 cc.
(dl.)	One deciliter equals.............	0.1	liter	100 cc.
(cl.)	One centiliter equals............	0.01	liter	10 cc.
(ml.)	One milliliter equals............	0.001	liter	1 cc.

(1 liter = 1.0567 qt.)

You can see the interrelationship of these three tables by considering a container filled with water. If this container is 10 centimeters long, 10 centimeters wide, and 10 centimeters high, it would contain 1,000 cubic centimeters (cc.), and this amount of water would weigh 1 Kilogram (Kg.), which is 1,000 grams, and it would also be 1 liter of water (1,000 cc.) or approximately 1 quart of our usual measure. (One liter equals 1.0567 qt.)

CONVERSION TABLE

There may be times when you will find it convenient to refer to the following conversion table in changing from the metric system to the English system, or vice versa, and for that reason we give a few of the common equivalents.

1 inch equals 2.54 centimeters
1 centimeter equals 0.394 inch
1 yard equals 0.914 meter
1 meter equals 1.09 yards
1 ounce equals 28.35 grams
1 quart equals 0.946 liter
1 liter equals 1.056 quarts
1 pound equals 453.6 grams
1 kilogram equals 2.2 pounds
1 pound equals 0.0155 cubic foot (water)
1 pound equals 0.12 gallon (water)
1 cubic foot equals 62.4 pounds (water)
1 gallon equals 8⅓ pounds (water)
1 cubic foot equals 7½ gallons
1 gallon equals 0.133 cubic foot

Chapter VI

SOURCES AND QUANTITIES OF SALTS USED

One of the essential things to know in starting nutrient culture is what chemical compounds to use to get the elements necessary for proper plant growth and where they may be obtained. In computing our formula we also must know the percentage of purity of the salts used to determine exactly how much to take. We give this information in the following pages. Since these chemical fertilizers vary in composition depending upon the manufacturing process, it is extremely important that you get an accurate analysis of the salt, stating the percentage of purity, the percentage of the desired element, and the percentage of fluorine present. (Fluorine is toxic in quantities above 1 per cent and *must* be avoided.)

Purity of Salts

Robert Withrow of Purdue University developed the following list of compounds showing the percentage of the desired element in each, the percentage of purity of the salt, and the gram-molecular weight corrected to the nearest 10 grams. You will remember that in the chapter on elementary chemistry we spoke of making up a definite formula by using the gram-molecular weight of the salt in 1,000 liters of water to get a millimole solution. We also mentioned that in making up the actual formula we make a correction of this gram-molecular weight in order to take impurities in the salts into account. As an example, using potassium nitrate KNO_3: $K = 39$, $N = 14$, $O_3 = 48$, or a total of 101. From the table of purity shown below we find that the grade we use is 95 per cent pure. Therefore 101 grams is just 95 per cent of the amount we need to make a millimole solution. ($101 \div 95 = 1.06 \times 100 = 106$ and, changing this to the nearest 10 grams, which is accurate enough for our purpose, we get 110 grams, as the table shows.) The other salts are calculated in the same manner. The table which follows is from Circular 232, 1937, Purdue University, to which we have added calcium nitrate

46

$(Ca(NO_3)_2)$ and monopotassium phosphate (KH_2PO_4). It will be found a great time-saver in making your calculations.

COMMERCIAL FERTILIZERS AS NUTRIENT SOLUTION SALTS

Nitrogen Salts	% N	% Purity	Grams/Mole
Ammonium sulfate $(NH_4)_2SO_4$...........	20	94	140
Ammonium nitrate, pure NH_4NO_3.......	35	98	80
Sodium nitrate $NaNO_3$................	16	97	90
Potassium nitrate KNO_3..............	13	95	110
Calcium nitrate $Ca(NO_3)_2$..............	15.5	70*	260
Calcium nitrate $Ca (NO_3)_2$.............	15	90†	180

Phosphate Salts ‡	% P_2O_5	% Purity	Grams/Mole
Monocalcium phosphate $CaH_4(PO_4)_2 \cdot H_2O$ (double superphosphate)..............	48	75*	310
Monocalcium phosphate $CaH_4(PO_4)_2 \cdot H_2O$ (food grade)........................	55	92*	270
Monopotassium phosphate KH_2PO_4......	....	97	140

Potassium Salts	% K_2O	% Purity	Grams/Mole
Potassium nitrate KNO_3................	44	95	110
Potassium sulfate K_2SO_4................	48	90	200
Potassium chloride KCl.................	60	95	80

Magnesium Salts		% Purity	Grams/Mole
Magnesium sulfate $MgSO_4 \cdot 7H_2O$ (epsom salts, tech.)...		45*	260
Magnesium sulfate $MgSO_4$ (anhydrous)..............		92	130

Calcium Salts		% Purity	Grams/Mole
Calcium chloride $CaCl_2$............................		75*	150
Calcium sulfate $CaSO_4$ (gypsum)....................		70*	190

* The purity is calculated on the basis of the designated formula. Water of crystallization is considered as impurity. CAUTION: In making your calculations be sure to use the exact formula for the salt employed in making up your nutrient solution when you figure the gram-molecular weight. For example, you will notice magnesium sulfate (epsom salts) has 260 grams per mole, whereas magnesium sulfate (anhydrous) has 130 grams per mole.

† The calcium nitrate we use comes from the Synthetic Nitrogen Products Company and is 90 per cent pure.

‡ Ammonium phosphate is not listed because the fertilizer grades tested are high in fluorine.

SOURCES OF CHEMICALS

In obtaining the proper salts we have found that the following sources are reliable. No doubt there are many others who can be depended upon equally well, but we caution you *first* to get an analysis from the manufacturer of the salt, and check whether it is of proper purity and contains no toxic substances.

Armour and Company (offices in principal cities) can furnish ammonium sulfate, potassium sulfate.

Synthetic Nitrogen Products Company, 85 Madison Avenue, New York City, can furnish ammonium sulfate, calcium nitrate.

Monsanto Chemical Company, St. Louis, Missouri, can furnish
monocalcium phosphate (food grade).

Victor Chemical Works, 141 West Jackson Boulevard, Chicago,
Illinois, can furnish triple superphosphate, monopotassium phosphate, monocalcium phosphate (food grade).

Baugh and Sons Company, Baltimore, Maryland, can furnish magnesium sulfate.

Dow Chemical Company, Midland, Michigan, can furnish magnesium sulfate.

McKesson & Robbins, Inc., 540 W. Randolph St., Chicago, Illinois,
can furnish magnesium sulfate, iron sulfate, manganese sulfate.

F. W. Berk & Co., Inc., 420 Lexington Avenue, New York City,
can furnish potassium nitrate.

Central Chemical, 4100 S. Ashland Ave., Chicago, Illinois, can
furnish nitric acid, sulfuric acid, hydrochloric acid.

ANALYSIS OF CHEMICALS

A number of firms which sell chemical fertilizer salts advertise
that their products contain a great number of chemical elements other

FIG. 19. A balance of this type is highly desirable. It must be sensitive, of large
capacity, and preferably have a scoop for weighing chemicals.

than those ordinarily supposed to be represented in the salt. These
other chemicals usually consist of the minor elements and for that
reason there is an advantage in nutrient culture in using such salts.
We do not have to add these minor elements as a rule, since they are
usually present as impurities in this grade of chemical. We show
below several typical analyses as given by the manufacturer or dis-
tributor. Notice the amount of minor elements present even though
the chemicals may be food-grade quality.

From the Synthetic Nitrogen Products Company we get this analysis:

CALCIUM NITRATE (FERTILIZER GRADE) 15% NITROGEN

	Per Cent
NH_4NO_3	4.7
H_2O	13.1
$Ca(NO_3)_2$	82.0
NH_4	1.07
NO_3	67.01
Ca	20.20
Insoluble acid	.01
Al_2O_3 plus Fe_2O_3	.01
Mg	.04
Na	.07
Cl	.01
SO_4	.05
H_2O	remainder
N	15.97

From the Armour Fertilizer Works we get this analysis:

AMMONIUM SULFATE (FERTILIZER GRADE)

	Per Cent
$(NH_4)_2SO_4$	99.65
$Fe_2(SO_4)_3$	0.10
Insoluble	0.05
Moisture	0.10

From the Monsanto Chemical Company we get the following analysis:

MONOCALCIUM PHOSPHATE

	Per Cent
Free acid	0.
Phosphate of lime	99.0
Monocalcium phosphate	89.5
Dicalcium phosphate	9.5
$CaSO_4$	0.42
$FePO_4$	0.12
$AlPO_4$	0.30
Moisture	0.28
Total P_2O_5	55.7
Soluble P_2O_5	50.4
CaO	22.0

	P P M
As_2O_3	0.2
Pb	1.0
Fluorine	15.0

From the Victor Chemical Works we get this analysis:

VICTOR TRIPLE SUPERPHOSPHATE

	Per Cent
Total phosphate P_2O_5	49.50
Insoluble phosphate P_2O_5	0.60
Available phosphate P_2O_5	48.90
Water-soluble phosphate P_2O_5	44.20
Free phosphate acid	1.20
Moisture	2.37
Chromium	0.005
Arsenic, As_2O_3	0.012
Calcium as CaO	19.10
Magnesium as MgO	0.16
Silica as SiO_2	4.82
Oxide of iron	1.03
Alumina	0.99
Potash as K_2O	0.55
Vanadium	0.002
Fluorine	0.856
Sulfur	0.54
Copper	0.003
Lead	0.02
Manganese	0.05
Zinc	0.0147
Boron as B_2O_3	0.0049

From the Victor Chemical Works we get this analysis:

MONOPOTASSIUM PHOSPHATE

	Per Cent
P_2O_5	51.10
K_2O	35.00
SO_3	0.18
$FePO_4$	0.18
$AlPO_4$	0.12
Chlorine	0.50

From the Armour Fertilizer Works we have this analysis:

POTASSIUM SULFATE

	Per Cent
Potassium sulfate	92.50
Potassium chloride	1.60
Magnesium sulfate	2.70
Magnesium chloride	1.00
Sodium chloride	1.20
Insoluble	0.30
Moisture	0.60

From the Baugh and Sons Company, Baltimore, Maryland, we have this analysis:

MAGNESIUM SULFATE (ANHYDROUS)

	Per Cent
$MgSO_4$	90.38
H_2O	0.78
Insoluble	1.03
NaCl	0.03
K_2SO_4	0.84
$CaSO_4$	0.96
$CaCO_3$	5.98

From McKesson & Robbins, Inc., Chicago, Illinois, we have the following analyses:

MAGNESIUM SULFATE (EPSOM SALTS)

$MgSO_4 \cdot 7H_2O$	not less than 99.5%
$MgSO_4$	more than 48.5%

MANGANESE SULFATE (Purified 90-95% $MnSO_4$)
(Powdered form)

Manganese sulfate (anhydrous)	90-95%
Calcium	Trace
Magnesium	Trace
Iron	Trace
Phosphorus	None
Insoluble matter	None
Balance moisture	None

FERROUS SULFATE OF IRON—FLOUR

	Per Cent
$FeSO_4 \cdot 7H_2O$	105.53
H_2SO_4	0.013
(Free acid)	
Fe (ferric)	Trace
Fe (ferrous)	21.24
H_2O	42.23

Average water content of the various grades of sulfate of iron, 42 to 43%.

F. W. Berk and Co., Inc., New York City, submit this analysis on a fertilizer which they sell under the trade name of Potnit:

POTASSIUM NITRATE

	Per Cent
KNO_3	95.61
K_2O	44.54
N	13.36
S	0.75
Cl	0.25
Moisture	0.13

The following analyses of acids represent average acids as supplied by the Central Chemical, Chicago, Illinois:

18° MURIATIC (HYDROCHLORIC) ACID

° Baumé	18.0°-18.3°
HCl	27.7%-27.0%
As	less than 0.5 ppm.
Pb	0.3 ppm.
Fe	0.001-0.002%
H_2SO_4	0.15 -1.00 %

66° SULFURIC ACID

° Baumé	66.0°
Specific gravity	1.835
H_2SO_4	93.0-93.2%
Pt	None
As	None
Mn	0.00005%
Fe	0.002-0.005%
Cu	None
Cl_2	None
Total oxidizable matter ($KMnO_4$)	0.0004-0.0008%

38° NITRIC ACID

° Baumé	38.0°-38.25°
HNO_3	56.5%-57.00%
As	None
Fe	0.005%
Pb	0.8 ppm.
Sulfuric acid	Trace
Chlorine	Trace
N_2O_3	Trace

CALCULATING WEIGHT OF SALTS USED

We now come to the point where we apply some of the facts we have learned. We must calculate the exact weight of each salt that our formula calls for, making this calculation on the basis of the size of the tank we will use in our installation. For example, let us assume that our tank is 20 feet by 5 feet by 4 feet. Since it is easier to make our calculations if we use the metric system, we find the volume of this tank in liters. To do this we need to convert these measurements to centimeters. By referring to the metric table we find that the conversion factor for this is 2.54 (1 inch equals 2.54 cm.). Therefore our calculation is:

20 (ft.) $\times$ 12 (in.) $\times$ 2.54 (conversion factor) = 609.6 cm. (length)
5 (ft.) $\times$ 12 (in.) $\times$ 2.54 (conversion factor) = 152.4 cm. (width)
4 (ft.) $\times$ 12 (in.) $\times$ 2.54 (conversion factor) = 121.9 cm. (depth)
609.6 cm. $\times$ 152.4 cm. $\times$ 121.9 cm. = 11,324,880 cubic centimeters (cc.)
11,324,880 cc. $\div$ 1,000 cc. = 11,324 liters, or, for our purpose, 11,300 liters

Our problem now is to determine the number of grams of each salt that will be needed according to our formula for a tank of this size. Suppose that our formula reads as follows:

SALT	MILLIMOLE
Calcium nitrate $Ca(NO_3)_2$	6
Potassium nitrate KNO_3	8
Magnesium sulfate $MgSO_4$	2
Double superphosphate $CaH_4(PO_4)_2$	2

Referring to the table of purity, we find that our calcium nitrate is only 90 per cent pure, and that it requires 180 grams to make a millimole solution in 1,000 liters. Hence it will require 6 times this much or 1,080 grams to make a 6 millimole solution in 1,000 liters. Our tank holds 11.3 thousand liters, so for a 6 millimole solution we need to weigh out 12,204 grams (1,080 $\times$ 11.3 = 12,204) of calcium nitrate. We learned before that 1 gram of any element in 1,000 liters of solution equals 1 part per million (ppm.) of that element in solution. From our table of atomic weights, we find that the atomic weight of nitrogen is 14. From the chemical formula of this salt we notice that there are two atoms of nitrogen in each molecule of the salt $(NO_3)_2$. Since we use 6 gram-molecules in making up our solution, we have $(2 \times 14 \times 6)$ 168 ppm. of nitrogen in our solution.

Next we calculate the amount of potassium nitrate to use in our tank in just the same fashion. We find that this salt is 95 per cent pure, and that it requires 110 grams per 1,000 liters for a 1 millimole solution. Our formula calls for an 8 millimole solution, so we have this calculation:

110	$\times$	8	$\times$	11.3	=	9944
(No. grams per 1,000 liters per 1 millimole)		(No. millimole required by formula)		(No. 1,000 liters in our tank)		(Grams to make an 8 millimole solution in our tank)

Therefore it requires 9,944 grams of potassium nitrate to make up that portion of our formula. To find the parts per million of both potassium and nitrogen we proceed as before. Potassium nitrate (KNO_3)

has one atom of potassium (K), and one atom of nitrogen (N), in each molecule. Since the weight of potassium is 39, we have (39 × 8 = 312) 312 ppm. of potassium. The weight of nitrogen is 14, so we have (14 × 8 = 112) 112 parts of nitrogen from this salt. We already have 168 ppm. of nitrogen from the calcium nitrate, so that now with these two salts in the solution we have 280 ppm. of nitrogen.

Proceeding in the same way we find that magnesium sulfate is 45 per cent pure and requires 260 grams per millimole per 1,000 liters. Therefore we have this calculation:

260 × 2 × 11.3 = 5,876 grams of magnesium sulfate to supply that part of our formula. This gives us (24 × 2) 48 ppm. of magnesium.

The amount of double superphosphate needed is figured in the same way:

310 × 2 × 11.3 = 7,006 grams of calcium phosphate $(CaH_4(PO_4)_2)$ for our tank. This gives (2 × 31 × 2) 124 ppm. of phosphorus.

From the facts determined by the above calculations we can make up a very convenient table which will be useful and save much time in the future. This table shows the formula used in our tank, the parts per million of each principal element, and the number of grams of the salt necessary to use in a tank of the size we have assumed.

This same method of calculating the required grams of salt and the parts per million can be used with any formula. It is much more convenient if you will make a table of this sort for each formula that you use and for each size of tank that you have. This saves all the time and effort of recalculating each time the solution is adjusted in the tank. We also find it convenient to have the table include a column showing the number of grams of the salt required to give 1 ppm. in the tank. This is obtained by simply dividing the number of grams of the salt required for the tank by the number of parts per million that quantity of salt gives. Referring to the table we find that 12,204 grams of $Ca(NO_3)_2$ gives 168 ppm. Therefore, 12,204 ÷ 168 = 72.6 grams, or, using the nearest gram, we say 73 grams of calcium nitrate in the tank will give 1 ppm. of nitrogen. When the season of the year arrives when we want to increase our nitrogen 50 ppm. we need only multiply this 73 grams by 50 (73 × 50 = 3,650) and find that we need to add 3,650 grams of calcium nitrate to bring the solution to the proper balance. In the same way for the salt KNO_3 to find the number of grams required for 1 ppm. of nitrogen

$(9,944 \div 112 = 88.7)$ or 89 grams to give 1 ppm. of nitrogen and $(9,944 \div 312 = 31.8)$ or 32 grams to give 1 ppm. of potassium (K). Likewise, for $MgSO_4$ $(5,876 \div 48 = 122)$, 122 grams for 1 ppm. of Mg, and for $CaH_4(PO_4)_2$ $(7,006 \div 124 = 56)$, 56 grams for 1 ppm. of P.

After you have calculated the quantity of each salt necessary for the tank of the size you have constructed, the next step is to weigh it out. For this a very sensitive balance is needed. Unless you are operating on a small experimental basis, we urge you to buy an accurate balance which is sensitive to $\frac{1}{2}$ gram and has a capacity of at least 7 Kilograms (15 lb.), preferably 14 Kilograms (30 lb.). Such a balance should be provided with a scoop for the chemicals and a metal platform for the weights. Be sure to specify metric weights when ordering.

We caution you to be accurate in weighing the chemical compounds. Weigh each compound separately, and simply put them together in a porcelain-lined bucket. When all the salts are weighed and put in this pail, hang it over the edge of the empty nutrient tank and fasten an ordinary hose so that the water gradually washes the salts out of the pail into the tank. Any water that is suitable for watering greenhouse plants is satisfactory for making the solution. The pH of the water ordinarily is not important as the pH of the solution is adjusted to the proper point before the solution is fed to the plants.

There has been a great deal of mystery built up about getting the salts into solution, but we have found that the above method requires no attention and is entirely satisfactory. After the salts have been washed out of the pail into the tank enough water should be added to fill the tank to the point required for the bench capacities. This point should be marked plainly, with a white paint that contains no oil, bismuth, or coal-tar derivatives, on the inside of the tank so that the level of the solution can readily be maintained.*

The table below is an example of the kind you should prepare for each different size of tank which you use and each salt in the formula you select.

Salt	Milli-mole	Gram/Mole	PPM.	Grams Required for the Tank	Grams to Give 1 PPM.
Ca(NO₃)₂..........	6	180	168 (N)	12,204	73
KNO₃.............	8	110	312 (K)	9,944	32
			112 (N)		89
MgSO₄............	2	260	48 (Mg)	5,876	122
CaH₄(PO₄)₂.......	2	310	124 (P)	7,006	56

*Put aside a gallon sample of the original solution made for each tank. This is your known standard solution for later comparison and testing.

Chapter VII

NUTRIENT-SOLUTION FORMULAS

In introducing the actual solution formula, we believe that some general remarks on the subject will be appropriate. As we know, plants acquire their raw foods (chemicals) from the soil solution when they are grown in soil. Changing this feeding operation from soil to nutrient solutions is not a radical step. Whether the plant gets its nitrogen, potassium, and phosphorus from the soil or from a pure solution makes very little difference so long as it gets them in the proper form and amount.

In soil culture, if your procedure is not correct, the plant warns you with certain symptoms, and you then take steps to correct the difficulties. In the same way with nutrients, the plant warns you, and you change the solution to remedy the situation. You need have no more fear of losing your crop with nutrients than when growing in soil. Unless you do something radically wrong, you will have plenty of time to adjust the solution to the needs of the crop. In fact, usually a crop answers to corrective measures much more quickly in nutrients than in soil culture.

Just as there are differences of opinion on proper fertilizers, and methods of growing in soil, so there are differences of opinion on formulas and methods of procedure with nutrient culture. We will mention several theories and will stress the one we believe to have great superiority. Some men who have been working with nutrients have been seeking a formula that could be used throughout the entire growing season. Our experience and the experience of many others would indicate that this is not feasible. In certain sections of the country where the daylight periods are of somewhat uniform length and where the intensity of the sunlight is not affected by much cloudy weather, it may be possible to use the same solution with little or no change over a long period of time. In our climate, in the Middle West, the days are much shorter in winter than in summer. At certain periods we may have several months of cloudy weather. It is against all the principles of plant physiology to assume that the same solution would produce the best growth under such widely varying conditions.

METHODS OF CONTROLLING GROWTH

Several methods have been devised by different investigators in an attempt to counteract the effect of varying light and temperature conditions. Some have tried increasing the concentration of the nutrient solution until it is so high that the plants cannot absorb water freely. The principle involved in this procedure depends upon osmosis, which is the way the nutrients get into the plant cells. In this way it is possible to reduce the amount of nutrients going into the plant by increasing the concentration of the nutrient salts in the tank. Most investigators recommend not increasing the concentration higher than three times the normal summer concentration. We tried increasing the concentration one year but found the method too expensive. It cost too much to increase the concentration three times normal, and the cost of maintaining it at this high level was prohibitive. Although by this theory the plants do not use as much of the fertilizer salts when they are grown in high concentration, nevertheless the salts disappear and must be replaced in large quantities to keep the concentration at this point. The salts apparently unite with or precipitate in the cinders and subsequently must be leached out and thus lost, constituting another unnecessary expense. The following year we worked on the nitrogen-potassium balance method and found it more satisfactory; it required only one-third as much fertilizer salts as the method of the previous year.

Others have tried reducing the number of feedings during adverse growing conditions. Instead of feeding three times daily, the feedings are limited to one in several days. This works on the same principle as watering the benches in soil culture. The house, after being watered, has a lower concentration of salts than it has a few days after drying out. The same principle applies when the cinders or gravel are flooded at irregular periods. If you should use this method, we caution you to make leaf tests regularly until you can recognize various plant symptoms and know just how to regulate the feedings. *Nitrogen* especially should be watched. Great care should be exercised to see that the plants do not wilt on hot sunny days, thus causing serious injury. Methods of leaf-testing will be given in detail in Chapter X.

We believe that the method which we have developed is superior to either of those mentioned above. Our method is to vary the proportions of elements in the solution. Nitrogen and potassium particularly need to be kept in balance during the winter days. Their relative proportion depends, we believe, on the intensity and amount of sunlight available. With our method we have a fine control of all growing factors. We find that within 8 hours we can determine whether a plant is reacting properly to the adjusted solution. Others who have tried a similar method of regulating the solution have had very satisfactory results. Our work would indicate that plants should be divided into two classes: (1) the hardwooded plants, such as roses and gardenias; and (2) the softwooded plants, such as carnations, chrysanthemums, stocks, feverfew, and tomatoes.

The two classes differ in their requirements, and this difference necessitates a variation in solution formula. The same solution can probably be used on both classes of plants but at different times of the year. As an example, the solution might be right for the hardwooded group in June, July, and August, but might not be right for the softwooded group until September, October, and November. We believe that there are sections of the United States where in all probability one solution will be satisfactory throughout the entire year for practically all crops. The sections of the country where this procedure has been most successful are those where there is practically no cloudy weather and where there is not too great a variation in the hours of available sunshine. From our experience, we believe that, even if we had no cloudy weather, it would still be better to vary the solutions with the changing seasons. We have about eight hours more sunshine each day in summer than in winter, and for that reason a plant can and does use more nitrogen during the long days than during the short ones.

As mentioned before, one of the factors that governs the choice of a solution depends to some extent on whether the plant builds softwood or hardwood. We find that the hardwooded plants require more potassium then the softwooded ones. The softwooded crops may again be divided into those which prefer an abundance of nitrogen and those which need only a moderate amount. Stocks, feverfew, carnations, and chrysanthemums all do well in the same solution and all require an abundance of nitrogen. Snapdragons, however, require much less nitrogen. Tomatoes are a softwooded crop, yet they do exceptionally well in the solution used for roses. They require not only less nitrogen but also more potassium during the fall and winter. One of the most

PLATE II

This section of bench shows remarkable yield of "New Globe" tomatoes—
ripe fruits picked 62 days after benching. Standard summer solution was used
at the beginning (p. 34); in the middle of July nitrogen was increased about
100 ppm.; toward the end of September nitrogen was decreased to the original
concentration and potassium was increased to 150 ppm. A small amount of
copper sulfate was added to the tank about once each month. About 15 ppm.
of iron was applied each week by dissolving the proper amount in a quart of
water and sprinkling the surface of the bench. About half this quantity of
manganese was applied with the iron twice a month.

satisfying factors in growing with nutrients is the accuracy with which one can judge the needs of the plant and properly adjust the solution to get a high-quality crop.

As an example of this crop control we might mention our experience with tomatoes. During the dark days of early January the fruit became watery. We knew of two factors that could cause this in *soil culture*: either improper temperature or too much water. Assuming these same factors would apply to nutrient culture as well, we carefully checked our temperature, which was found to be correct. We then decided that the other factor, too much water, was the fault, and so with one house we shut off the feedings completely for twenty-three days. The plants were uninjured and the fruit hardened up slightly but not enough. On the other houses, at the same time that we stopped the feedings on the first house, we tried changing the concentration of potassium, as we had learned from other crops that potassium serves to harden the growth. Accordingly we increased the potassium from 660 ppm. to 1,000 ppm., with the result that within five days the fruit was in proper marketable condition. The flavor was also changed and seemed to be sweeter. We believe that 800 ppm. to 850 ppm. applied before the trouble developed would have prevented it. We believe that the proper balance between nitrogen and potassium can be determined in advance by reference to the chart on this nitrogen-potassium balance.

Twelve Tested Formulas

Any of the formulas recommended by the various experiment stations will give a good basic solution to work with, either for certain crops or for specific periods of the year, and may be used as recommended. Variations may be made as the operator deems necessary. On the following pages we give a number of the best formulas and the source from which they were obtained. You will notice that there is a great variation in both the kind and amount of the various salts used.

Two solutions used with great success by Dr. John Arthur, of Boyce Thompson Institute, are as follows:

1. The first is a Shive three salt solution.

Compound		%	PPM.
Calcium nitrate	$Ca(NO_3)_2$	0.085	850
Potassium acid phosphate	KH_2PO_4	0.245	2,450
Magnesium sulfate	$MgSO_4$	0.180	1,800

2. Another solution is composed of acids and bases.

Compound		%	PPM.
Sulfuric acid	H_2SO_4	0.0379	379
Nitric acid	HNO_3	0.0277	277
Phosphoric acid	H_3PO_4	0.0394	394
Potassium hydroxide	KOH	0.0143	143
Ammonium hydroxide	NH_4OH	0.0155	155
Calcium oxide	$CaO \cdot H_2O$	0.0140	140
Magnesium oxide	MgO	0.0165	165

To each of these solutions should be added traces of iron, boron, and manganese. The compounds used in these formulas should be chemically pure salts rather than fertilizer grade.

From the New Jersey Experiment Station, we have the following solution recommended by R. B. Farnham and R. P. White for the crops which precede the formula. The acidity must be varied as shown.

For roses, pH 6.0-7.0; carnations, pH 5.5-6.5; gardenias, pH 4.5-5.0. In 100 gallons of solution use the number of grams shown in column A; in 1,000 liters, use the amount shown in column B.

	A	B
Ammonium sulfate	60 g.	150 g.
Potassium monobasic phosphate	114 g.	285 g.
Magnesium sulfate	280 g.	570 g.
Calcium nitrate	972 g.	2,430 g.

Another solution from the same source recommended for other crops should have the acidity: for sweet peas, pH 6.0-7.0; for snapdragons, pH 5.5-6.5; and for most other crops, pH 5.5-6.5. The amount of salts used in 100 gallons of solution is given in column A, and the amount for 1,000 liters is given in column B.

	A	B
Potassium monobasic phosphate	243 g.	608 g.
Calcium nitrate	864 g.	2,260 g.
Magnesium sulfate	451 g.	1,127 g.

Robert Withrow of Purdue University has worked with a number of solutions, the most famous of which are his 2D and 2E. We also give several other formulas that he has worked out. Fertilizer-grade salts are used in these formulas.

Solution 2C

Compound		Millimole	Grams per 1,000 liters
Magnesium sulfate	$MgSO_4$	1	260
Treble superphosphate	$CaH_4(PO_4)_2$	1	310
Potassium nitrate	KNO_3	8	880
Ammonium sulfate	$(NH_4)_2SO_4$	2	280

Solution 2D

Compound		Millimole	Grams per 1,000 liters
Magnesium sulfate (anhydrous)	$MgSO_4$	0.5	65
Treble superphosphate	$CaH_4(PO_4)_2$	0.5	155
Potassium nitrate	KNO_3	10.	1,100
Calcium sulfate (agricultural)	$CaSO_4$	4.	760
Ammonium sulfate	$(NH_4)_2SO_4$	1.	140

Solution 1E

Magnesium sulfate (anhydrous)	$MgSO_4$	4.	520
Treble superphosphate	$CaH_4(PO_4)_2$	2.	620
Potassium nitrate	KNO_3	6.	660
Calcium nitrate	$Ca(NO_3)_2$	4.	720
Ammonium sulfate	$(NH_4)_2SO_4$	0.5	70

Solution 2E

Magnesium sulfate (anhydrous)	$MgSO_4$	0.5	65
Treble superphosphate	$CaH_4(PO_4)_2$	0.5	155
Potassium nitrate	KNO_3	6.	660
Calcium nitrate	$Ca(NO_3)_2$	4.	720
Ammonium sulfate	$(NH_4)_2SO_4$	2.	160

From the Ohio State Experiment Station we get the following three formulas:

Solution W. P.

	Grams per 1,000 gallons	Grams per 1,000 liters
Potassium nitrate	2,632	608
Ammonium sulfate	439	110
Magnesium sulfate	2,043	511
Monocalcium phosphate	1,090	282
Calcium sulfate	4,856	1,214

Solution 2E

	Ounces per 60 gallons	Grams per 60 gallons	Grams per 1,000 liters
Potassium nitrate	6	168	672
Ammonium sulfate	1½	43	168
Magnesium sulfate	½	14	56
Monocalcium phosphate	1	28	112
Calcium nitrate	1	28	112

Ferrous sulfate, 3 teaspoonfuls; manganese sulfate, 1% solution, 300 cc.

SOLUTION 2 W. P.

	Ounces per 60 gallons	Grams per 60 gallons	Grams per 1,000 liters
Potassium nitrate	12	336	1,344
Ammonium sulfate	1½	42	168
Magnesium sulfate	9	252	1,008
Monocalcium phosphate	4½	126	504
Calcium sulfate	21	588	2,354

Ferrous sulfate, 3 teaspoonfuls; manganese sulfate, 1% solution, 300 cc.

Another solution originated at the Central Experimental Farm, Ottawa, Ontario. It proved highly satisfactory when used by H. Hill and M. B. Davis for growing chrysanthemums.

	Grams per 50 gallons	Grams per 1,000 liters
Magnesium sulfate	247.2	1,236
Potassium phosphate monobasic	134.5	672.5
Calcium chloride	275.	1,375
Potassium nitrate	300.6	1,503
Ammonium nitrate	675.	3,375

You may have noticed a great variation in the twelve formulas we have given; yet basically they are quite similar. From the reports of those who have used these solutions, fine results have been obtained. Any one of them would probably be satisfactory to start with, provided that you vary it as you go along to meet the varying conditions of your crop. In view of the multiplicity of formulas you may find it difficult to know just how to start. We know of one large greenhouse establishment that selected a solution formula and grew a great number of miscellaneous crops in it the first year. The following year, they selected the crops which did best, discontinuing the poorer, and had an excellent and profitable year. Another way of starting, and we believe the best way, is to grow the crop with which you have had the most experience, select a solution that agrees with it, and then by frequent testing keep this solution in proper balance for the best results. Incidentally we might mention that the hardwooded crops, such as roses and gardenias, seem to present more difficulties than the miscellaneous crops in the softwooded group.

RECORDING DATA

If you keep detailed and accurate records of your work, we believe that you will experience little difficulty. Starting with your original solution, make a record of the kind and amount of the various chemicals used. An ordinary diary with a page for each day is fine for the purpose, and you will find your record invaluable later in handling the various problems that come up. We suggest that you put down the amount and kind of chemicals added from time to time, also record what each of your tests shows as to the condition both of your solution and of your plants. It is wise to note the weather conditions, outside and inside temperatures, and whether the day was predominately cloudy or sunny. You will find that there is a definite relation between the light intensity and duration, and the amount and kind of chemicals which the plant needs for maximum productiveness. A record of both quantity and quality of the crop as gathered will enable you to tell whether you are getting the maximum results possible. If you have the same crop growing in soil, select a similar amount of space and determine by comparison which method gives the greater return. By regular leaf tests, solution tests, and by watching the various symptoms shown in the plant, a grower will soon learn the exact requirements of his crop. If you can grow a good crop in soil, you can easily learn to grow a better one in nutrients, because much of the guesswork is taken out of the job when you make your accurate tests. If you have kept detailed records and have been successful one year, you can be certain that the following year you will get the same results. This is not true in soil culture, because, first of all, you start with an unknown medium—the soil, add what fertilizers you "think" are necessary, and then from time to time mulch the crop with another unknown, the fertilizer or manure. Speaking of the use of manure, that is one way that disease and insects frequently are introduced into your houses. One reason we experience greater freedom from insects and disease with nutrient culture is that we start with clean, sterile benches and add only pure, uncontaminated chemicals. Neither the solution nor the cinders presents a very good medium for the breeding of insects or disease.

DISCARDING *vs.* REPLENISHING SOLUTIONS

The next thing to consider is the procedure in handling the solution. Practically everyone has adopted the method of mixing new fresh nutrients frequently and discarding the old solution. With this practice we disagree very decidedly. We believe it to be unnecessary, extravagant, and wasteful of time. If our solution tests prove anything, they certainly show that it is not wise to grow plants in a solution for a month and then discard it for a fresh solution. We find that *long* before a month has elapsed many of the necessary elements have been depleted. Some growers who have adopted the discard method have attempted to salvage the unused chemicals by applying the spent solution to some of their soil-grown crops. This may recover some of the chemicals, but it only stands to reason that the very chemicals the soil-grown crops need most have already been used by the nutrient-solution crop. So far as the soil-grown crop is concerned this procedure is not likely to result in any harm, but we doubt if it does as much good as the grower would like to believe.

We have found that by testing our solutions twice weekly, and replacing those salts that have been depleted, we have greater economy and a more rigid check on our nutrients. Why should one throw away a quantity of good unused nitrogen, phosphorus, or potassium when the solution can be restored to proper strength by adding a small amount of the depleted chemical? At first we tested our solution every day but found that the changes were so small that this was not necessary. Then we tried testing only once a week, but the changes were so great at times that the plants were suffering from lack of one or more important elements. We have learned that testing twice a week gives adequate control. During the summer days, we noticed that, between weekly tests, often as much as one-third of the nitrogen had been used and at times as much as one-half of the phosphorus. One of the objections raised to our method of replenishing salts as they are used is that some salts have a tendency to precipitate in the tanks and impurities may collect. Naturally some salts do precipitate, but solutions have been used in our tanks for more than a year without a complete change, apparently without injury to the crop. There is some precipitate in the tank, of course, but probably not so much as is supposed. An open tank cannot stand for a year without accumuulating some dust and other rubbish. Also some of the dust and dirt of the cinders no doubt gradually finds its way back to the tank. It may not be practical in some cases to use the same solution without a complete change for as long as a year, but certainly the factor governing the length of time the solution should be used is something other than precipitates, impurities, or weakened solution. By testing the foliage frequently, by watching the general appearance of the plant, and by regular twice-weekly tests of the solution, one should be able to grow crops in nutrient solutions with even more confidence than he would have were he growing them in soil.

Technic of the Nitrogen-Potassium Balance

The technic which we follow with our solutions, as we said, is vastly different from that followed by most people using nutrients, but we believe that our experience has proved our system capable of giving the finest results with the least outlay of time, money, and labor. Since all three of these are important items on the profit-and-loss statement, we believe that our method will show an increased profit.

In the following pages we want to mention a few of the facts which we have established during our work with nutrients. Roses may be fed, at any time, as much nitrogen as they can use *without storing it in the leaf*. If a test shows even a trace of nitrogen in the base of the petiole of a young leaf, too much nitrogen is being used.* If too much potassium is being used, the foliage and stems of the old wood become brittle; if the excess is continued, the parts will become so brittle that the leaves will snap off at the slightest touch. The difficulty arises in getting the proper balance between the nitrogen and the potassium. Whether this brittleness is due to an excess of potassium or to a deficiency of nitrogen we do not know, but it shows that the balance between the two elements is not correct and needs adjusting either by increasing the nitrogen, decreasing the potassium, or both. By balance we do not mean that a one-to-one ratio or a three-to-one ratio should be maintained at all times. It simply means that the effects of nitrogen and potassium counteract each other, and that a proper relation must be maintained. This ratio varies with the amount and quality of the light available to the plant. In the summer a rose plant may be able to use a solution containing 450 ppm. of nitrogen and does best if the solution contains about 170 ppm. of potassium (although this may be reduced to as little as 85 ppm. if no shading is used on the houses). In contrast, in winter, the plant will do best if the nitrogen is reduced to as little as 100 ppm. and the potassium increased to 800 ppm. or even more in prolonged dark weather. Tests of the nutrient solution in the summer frequently show that as much as one-third of the nitrogen has been used in a week, yet the plants will not give a leaf test for nitrogen. This proves that nitrogen is not being stored in the foliage. During the dark days of midwinter, if we keep our nutrient solution at a concentration of 100 ppm. of nitrogen, only very small quantities of the element will be taken from the solution, and it may be several weeks before any more nitrogen need be added to the tank. However, during this same period, if the potassium is kept at 450 ppm. we find that as much as one-fourth of the element has been used in a single week. If large amounts of potassium are being used, increase the concentration of the potassium salt. The plants can stand a concentration as great as 800-900 ppm. during dark weather.

* The nitrogen disclosed by this leaf test is nitrate nitrogen. Nitrogen in other forms, which is not indicated by this test, is always present in the leaf.

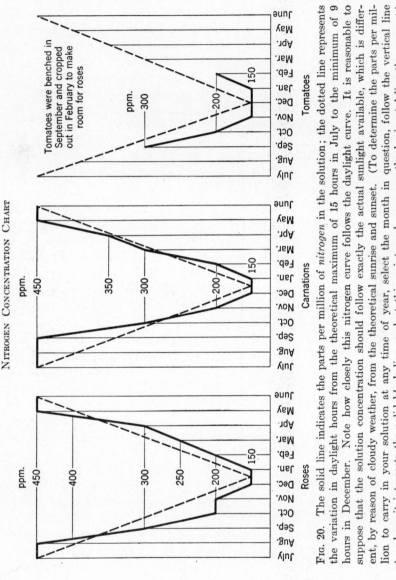

FIG. 20. The solid line indicates the parts per million of *nitrogen* in the solution; the dotted line represents the variation in daylight hours from the theoretical maximum of 15 hours in July to the minimum of 9 hours in December. Note how closely this nitrogen curve follows the daylight curve. It is reasonable to suppose that the solution concentration should follow exactly the actual sunlight available, which is different, by reason of cloudy weather, from the theoretical sunrise and sunset. (To determine the parts per million to carry in your solution at any time of year, select the month in question, follow the vertical line to where it intersects the solid black line, and at this point read across on the horizontal line to the amount.)

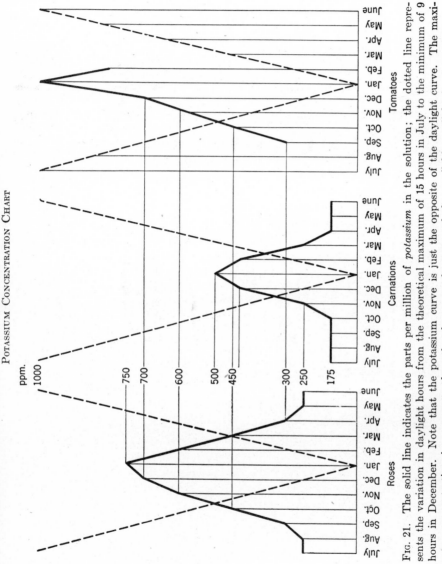

FIG. 21. The solid line indicates the parts per million of *potassium* in the solution; the dotted line represents the variation in daylight hours from the theoretical maximum of 15 hours in July to the minimum of 9 hours in December. Note that the potassium curve is just the opposite of the daylight curve. The maximum concentration is necessary when the days are shortest and the available sunlight is at a minimum

Carnations act in much the same way as roses, except that leaf tests cannot determine the amount of nitrogen used. Carnation leaves always give a nitrogen test. Their method of disclosing that an excess of nitrogen is being used is by a rank soft growth and weakened stems. An excess of potassium is shown in much the same way as with roses. The stems become so brittle that they break at the slightest touch at every node or joint. If these symptoms in the carnation are watched for, the nutrient may be regulated very easily. Carnations and roses are quite similar in their relative requirements of these two elements. Both need a small amount of nitrogen and a large amount of potassium in the winter; in summer, both like a large amount of nitrogen and a small amount of potassium. Your solution may contain as much as 400 ppm. of nitrogen and as little as 85 ppm. of potassium in the summer, whereas in the winter the nitrogen concentration should be between 100 and 150 ppm. and the potassium 400-600 ppm. in the darkest weather. Most other crops require a similar balance between the nitrogen and potassium—in summer plenty of nitrogen and a minimum of potassium; in winter plenty of potassium and a minimum of nitrogen.

Nitrogen-Potassium Charts *

We believe that the facts disclosed by the accompanying charts indicate the greatest advance toward the simplification of nutrient culture that has yet been made. In order that you may understand the full significance of the chart, we should like to mention how it was developed. During this early work with nutrient culture, the same difficulties that others have had in properly adjusting the solution to get a maximum fine crop were encountered. Using the "guess" method, there was trouble frequently. However, it was soon noticed that there seemed to be a definite need for more potassium and less nitrogen in the solution as the winter growing season advanced. It was also discovered that the addition of potassium had a tendency to counteract the bad effects of too much nitrogen in the solution. Also it was found that, when there were several consecutive bright days, the plants used much more nitrogen than at other times, and the ultimate conclusion was that there was a definite relationship between the amount and intensity of the sunlight available and the amount of nitrogen required.

* For many years practical growers have worked on the theory of a nitrogen-potassium balance in relation to light, as is evidenced by the different methods of feeding in summer and winter with their soil-grown crops, but very little work seems to have been done along this line by scientific investigators.

Accordingly, the following year, the sunlight factor was watched carefully; and nitrogen was fed during the sunny periods and allowed to diminish during the darker, cloudy weather. When the days were exceedingly dark for a long period of time and this dark period followed a series of very bright days, it was found that the nitrogen concentration was altogether too high, so that it was necessary to add potassium in sufficient quantities to counteract this excess nitrogen.

Bearing these facts in mind, if you will consult the Rose Chart you will find that, by watching the various deficiency symptoms and adjusting the solution month by month, the nitrogen was gradually dropped from 450 ppm. in July to 150 ppm. in December, and that the potassium concentration was gradually increased from 250 ppm. in July to 750 ppm. in December. As you will notice, this resulted in a somewhat irregular curve, because the adjustment was not made until *after* the deficiency symptom was evident. Since the second half of the winter growing season is just the reverse in relative light condition to the first half of the winter growing season, it was assumed that, if this theory was correct, the nitrogen-potassium balance could be adjusted in advance by projecting this curve for the future months and following it exactly. In this way the solution could be adjusted *before* the deficiency symptoms developed. After projecting this curve, all adjustments in the solution were made automatically as the chart called for them, regardless of plant symptoms, and the result was that no difficulties were encountered. During the second half of the year this curve shows as a straight line because the nitrogen was built up regularly each month from 150 ppm. in December to 450 ppm. in July and the potassium was decreased steadily each month from 750 ppm. in December to 250 ppm. in July. The reason for the curve's running horizontally during July and August, and during May and June, is that the houses were shaded during these months, as is customary to prevent excessive temperatures. This naturally keeps the light factor more or less uniform during this period.

We also show a chart for carnations, in which you will notice that the roses definitely require more potassium at all times than the carnations. Further you will notice that the nitrogen requirements of both crops are very similar. In fact, the maximum and minimum requirements seem to be identical, although there is a slight variation at other times of the year.

On the chart for tomatoes you will notice that only part of a year is shown. This is due to the fact that they were used as a fill-in crop, were not benched until September, and were discarded in February.

Strange as it may seem, the tomatoes were grown in the identical solution as the roses, until January. We had always harbored the idea that one of the factors governing the solution formula was whether the plant made hardwood or softwood, but the tomatoes did so well in the same solution as the roses that it raised a big question whether that was a factor. However, in December when the plants were setting a tremendous amount of fruit, we ran into difficulties. The tomatoes became watery, and as explained elsewhere in the text the solution to this problem turned out to be the addition of a large amount of potassium. This remedied the difficulty; within 5 days the fruit was again firm and of good color.

We do not show either magnesium or phosphorus on these charts because we carry them constantly at 60 ppm. and 70 ppm., respectively. We found that none of these crops require much magnesium, although it must be available, so we carry the magnesium rather low and test for it only every three or four weeks. All the crops seem to require a great deal of phosphorus and normally with such a requirement we would carry a high concentration of that salt. However, the salt which we use contains fluorine (F), which, as we mentioned, is highly toxic in high concentrations. For that reason we regularly carry a low concentration but add phosphorus after each test as we frequently find that as much as half of the phosphorus has been used in three days.

A chart similar to these can be worked out by each grower for his locality, on the basis of the relative light conditions. Although the exact charts which we illustrate may not be used without change in all parts of the country, we believe that they will serve as a guide and will probably give satisfactory results while one is working out his own. We are confident that if you will regulate your solution in accordance with such a chart you will find that growing satisfactory crops by the nutrient-culture method is extremely simple.

Magnesium and Phosphorus Requirements

Magnesium and phosphorus are essential elements in the solution at all times, but apparently they do not play so important a part in the general regulation of growth as nitrogen and potassium. If the test shows a moderate amount of each, it is probably sufficient, as 60 ppm. of magnesium and 70 ppm. of phosphorus seems to be about right. We maintain these figures during the entire year. If the food grade of salt is used, such as monocalcium phosphate, more may be added than of the triple superphosphate. The food grade contains very little fluorine. No injury was ever noticed even though the triple superphosphate was employed and the concentration was held for several months at 140 ppm. However, it would probably be safer to use a lower concentration than this of the triple superphosphate salt. If the plant seems to need the higher concentration we suggest that you use monocalcium phosphate.

When Robert Withrow started his investigations into nutrient solutions, he used the fertilizer grade of salts instead of the higher-priced food grade. Undoubtedly, as good plants can be grown with these cheaper fertilizers as with the higher-grade salts. The plant needs only the proper amount of the essential elements, and whether they come from relatively pure salts or those of fertilizer grade seems to make no difference. At the same time we frequently eliminate the necessity of adding some of the minor elements when we use the cheaper grade of salts, for these minor elements are often present in them as impurities and in sufficient quantities for the plant's use. Because ammonia interferes with the potassium test, we never use it, but get the entire supply of nitrogen as nitrates in either calcium nitrate or potassium nitrate.

Determine the amount of the element wanted in the solution by the general appearance of the plant or by test and feel free to supply the deficiency in the easiest and quickest way. If you need a higher concentration of nitrogen in the solution, why use two or three nitrogen salts, such as calcium nitrate, ammonium sulfate, and potassium nitrate, when either one of these salts in the proper amount would do the work? If you use several salts to supply the deficiency, you simply complicate the work of figuring the proper quantity to add. Different authorities disagree about the use of ammonium salts. Some claim that the plant uses the ammonia directly; others, that only nitrates are used. Until further evidence to the contrary is discovered, we shall continue to recommend nitrates because they simplify the task of testing for potassium. (We have found that a plant can utilize ammonia during the long bright days of summer, but during the dark short days of winter the ammonia has a toxic effect on the plant.) If, however, ammonium salts are used, we recommend that the concentration be kept between 10 and 20 ppm. of ammonium nitrogen, the balance of the nitrogen requirement being made up with nitrate salts. (See Circular 232, revised 1938, Purdue University.)

Iron Requirements

Iron presents a real difficulty. The hardwooded crops apparently require much more iron than the softwooded crops. Carnations, mums, tomatoes, stocks, etc., have never shown an iron deficiency in cinders, but roses soon show such a deficiency as indicated by a spotting of the leaves. This iron deficiency can be distinguished easily from nitrogen deficiency as the veins remain green while the interveinal spaces become yellowish and spotted. Nitrogen deficiency shows no spotting. Another difference is that, with iron deficiency, just the new growth shows the deficiency; the old foliage does not show it unless there was a deficiency when it was grown. If you are using nutrient culture on a large scale commercially, you will find that it is not practical to apply the iron with the regular solution. Iron has a great tendency to precipitate in the tank and in the benches as well. This precipitation can be checked to some extent by increasing the acidity of the solution, since iron has a tendency to precipitate more in an alkaline solution. However, this is not a good method, for even if you get the proper amount of iron to stay in solution in the tank you still have difficulties ahead. Iron has a tendency to precipitate in certain spots and will not distribute itself evenly throughout the benches. Some parts of the bench get too much iron and other parts too little. This gives a very spotted effect to the house. Some plants are of good color and others of poor color, showing a definite deficiency of this element. Increasing the amount of iron in the solution does no good as the element seems to keep building up the precipitate in certain spots until so much accumulates as to cause severe injury to the plants.

Method of Applying Iron

To overcome these various difficulties, we have adopted the method of sprinkling the iron solution over the surface of the cinders. This, of course, gives an even distribution, each plant getting its share, and all plants then show a fine even color. Although sprinkling the iron solution on in this fashion is another operation, and is done by hand, it is not so difficult as it may seem at first. Nearly every greenhouse is equipped with a good stationary spray system, and this can be used in the application of the iron solution. Simply mix in the spray tank, with 200 gallons of water, the amount of ferrous sulfate needed, and spray it on through the ordinary hose, without a nozzle. In this way a house 30 feet by 200 feet can be sprayed in about a half hour. To determine the correct amount of iron sulfate to use, calculate the number of grams of the salt needed to give the equivalent of 10-15 ppm. in the quantity of solution in the main solution tank. Then mix this quantity with the 200 gallons of water in the spray tank and water on the benches as above. In addition, if an application of manganese is needed, it can be applied at the same time as the iron by simply mixing the proper amount of manganese salt with the iron solution. Apparently these iron difficulties do not occur in small experimental installations where the distribution is confined to quite a small area, but the above method even on benches 200 feet long will relieve you of any worries about iron deficiencies.

Roses and gardenias require a large quantity of iron but prefer it in small doses given frequently. It should be applied at least once a week and preferably twice or even three times a week if needed. Manganese should be fed in much smaller quantities than iron. We find that an application once a week, using at each weekly application a quantity about one-fourth that of iron, is all that is needed. The regular fertilizer grade of nutrient salts apparently contains enough impurities, as is seen by their analysis, to care for all the other minor elements.

The acidity of the solution is important and should be checked regularly. You should maintain the acidity at the points recommended by R. B. Farnham and R. R. White which were mentioned earlier in this chapter. During the summer months probably little or no acid will have to be added. Later on, the benches may become too acid, in which event the acidity may be adjusted by adding sodium hydroxide to the tank solution.

As a final reminder, always bear in mind that there is a direct relation between the amount and intensity of the light and the amount of nitrogen the plant can use efficiently, and that the nitrogen and potassium must be kept in proper balance to conform to this light relationship.

Chapter VIII

FUNDAMENTALS OF PLANT PHYSIOLOGY

Just as we reviewed some of the elementary facts of chemistry, so it is important to renew in our minds some of the processes and mechanical functions of the growing plant. This information comes under the heading of plant physiology. By knowing something of these processes it is easier to determine just what is taking place and what effect nutrient solutions are having on the expected growth and development of the plant. A fertile seed contains a complete live plant in the dormant state, with enough stored food to carry it through the process of germination until it can establish itself in soil or other growing medium. The parent plant manufactured and stored in this tiny seed enough food to start it into growth and care for it until the seedling's own root system could take food from the soil or elsewhere.

Growth: Photosynthesis—Assimilation

When the temperature is right and enough moisture penetrates the seed coat, the compounds stored in the seed are converted into active plant foods and the young dormant plant in the seed starts growth. At this point it will be well to distinguish between the two very definite processes performed by a growing plant. In general, the popular idea of growth is the obvious increase in size that is noticed as the seedling develops into the mature plant. This part of the growth process results from cell division and elongation, and is accompanied by changes in external form and internal structure. Light is not necessary for this part of the growth process as may be seen by the fact that potatoes will grow in darkness. However, they will grow in darkness only until they have used up all the food stored in the tuber. For continued growth, the plant must manufacture more food. The ordinary green plant has only two sources from which it obtains raw food elements—the air, and the soil or solution. The first step in uniting these raw materials, known as photosynthesis, takes place only in the presence of sunlight or intense artificial light.

In this connection it might be well to mention that, though it is

74

possible to develop photosynthesis by artificial light, it requires an intensity of at least 400 foot-candles. Also, since there are these two definite processes, growth and photosynthesis, the ideal balance between light and darkness probably is that which obtains in summer when they are very nearly equally divided. It is at that time of year that we get the best all-round development. Most of the experiments with artificial light have shown that, though natural sunlight can be supplemented during the darker days, plants do need a dark period and will not grow satisfactorily in continuous light.* As a part of the process of photosynthesis, the leaves take in carbon dioxide from the air. This enters through small openings or pores called stomata. In most plants the stomata are found on the under surface of the leaf. The green coloring in the leaf, known as chlorophyll, is primarily responsible for this change of raw materials into carbohydrates. During photosynthesis, carbon dioxide is used and oxygen is liberated. In the absence of light the chlorophyll in the leaf becomes inactive and the manufacturing of carbohydrates ceases. Visible growth increases in the absence of light, and during this part of the process, when cell division or elongation takes place rapidly we have an opposite reaction as more oxygen is used and a greater amount of carbon dioxide is liberated by the plant. Respiration takes place in both darkness and light. After the carbohydrates are once formed the plant can apparently produce from them, regardless of light, most of the complex compounds which it needs. Under the influence of the living matter of the plant the simple carbohydrates produced in the leaves are united with the raw elements brought up from the roots to form protoplasm. This complex process is called assimilation.

Practically all mineral elements that are assimilated by the plant must go through the root system in solution. It is for that reason that all the elements we use in our nutrient solutions must be soluble in water. The roots grow out from the plant in search of food and water. At the end of the main roots are thousands of tiny root-hairs whose function it is to take up the raw elements and water. The large roots merely act as conveyors to get these raw materials to the stem and leaves. Some of the large roots may also act as storehouses for the manufactured food.

The plant has a simple circulation system. One set of tubes carries

* Experiments with light are being conducted today which seem to indicate that this dark period is not so important as was once supposed. See, for further discussion of this point, Dr. John Arthur's bulletin, "Biological Effects of Radiation," McGraw-Hill Book Company, New York.

the raw materials from the roots up to the leaves, and another set carries the manufactured foods downward from the leaves. The tubes that carry the materials up are known as the xylem; those that carry the food down are called the phloem. These tubes are not continuous but are made up of innumerable cells with permeable walls. See Fig. 22. A cross section of the stem of the ordinary plant with which

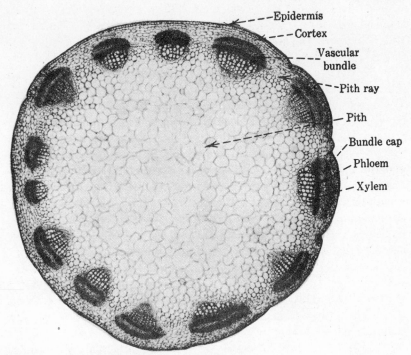

FIG. 22. A typical stem section of clover showing the structure of the vascular bundle. In some plants, such as corn, the vascular bundles are distributed throughout the pith; in others they are arranged in complete, concentric circles forming ultimately the annular rings which are seen readily in the hardwooded group, as in the cross section of a tree.

we are concerned shows under a microscope an outside protective layer called the bark, which protects the vital parts. Directly underneath this bark we find the phloem (the tubes which take the manufactured food downward); underneath the phloem we find the growing tissue of the plant—the cambium layer. The cambium layer surrounds the xylem (the tubes which take the raw materials up to the leaves); and this in turn surrounds the innermost substance—the pith.

MOVEMENT OF SOLUTIONS IN PLANTS

Since all minerals must pass into the plant in solution, it will be well to mention the three main forces by which solutions enter. First: *imbibition,* which is the process whereby water is absorbed by any organic body. This water is taken up and held by capillarity, or surface tension. This phenomenon is especially characteristic of colloidal material in the gel condition, as each particle of such substances has an affinity or attraction for water. The hardest wood may absorb water by imbibition; dry hard seed coats take up water by imbibition, which usually causes swelling. This process particularly is important in the activity of non-living cell walls.

Second: *osmosis,* which is a diffusion process whereby water moves through membranes or partitions. Water is a solvent and normally moves from a lesser to a greater concentration of the solute or salt solution. The solute itself, where permitted by nature of the membrane, normally moves from a region of greater to one of lesser concentration. This movement, which is wholly independent of any convection currents due to differences in temperature, implies a force which is termed osmotic pressure. It is this force combined with the force of imbibition which accounts for the inflow of water to the root-hair and the flow of water through the living cell wall or membrane. It is because of these phenomena and root pressure that water and nutrients are carried from the roots to the topmost branches of tall trees. At this point it is important to call attention to the fact that if our nutrient solution is too concentrated a reverse flow of water out of the plant and consequent wilting will result.

The third process of water transfer, *transpiration,* is really a transfer of water from the plant and is in the nature of evaporation, but as the process is closely related to the other two it will be considered here. In studying the cell structure of the leaf we find that there are certain openings known as *stomata* through which the inner leaf cells are in contact with the air. Air diffusing through these stomata comes in contact with moist cells in the leaf, and as a consequence some water is lost by evaporation. This moisture is then replaced from adjacent cells, and the process continues throughout the entire plant. In this way there is a continuous water movement through the plant. Nutrient salts move into the plant by diffusion more or less independently of water movement. There is a certain balance between the leaf and root surfaces.

PLANT STRUCTURE

If you will refer to the highly magnified cross section of the leaf shown, you will see that the leaf is a very complex structure, the necessity for which is understood when we consider the many important functions which leaves perform. See Fig. 23. Leaves play

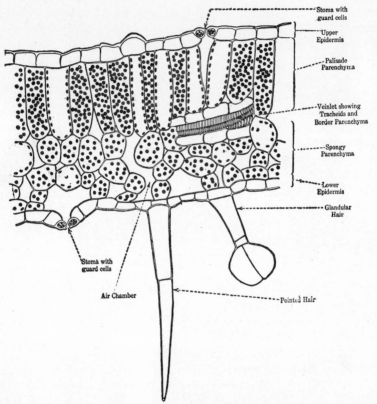

FIG. 23. A typical leaf section highly magnified. This shows the intercellular spaces, stomata, and chlorophyll.

the leading role in plant life since they manufacture carbohydrates (photosynthesis). This marvelous process is accomplished in some mysterious manner by the small green bodies which give the leaf its green color. These bodies contain the chlorophyll. Although the chemical composition of chlorophyll is known, scientists are still trying to discover the why and how of the process. The leaves perform another important role in plant life in the visible growth process. They take in oxygen and give off carbon dioxide, at the same time using up some of the food which previously had been manufactured during the process of photosynthesis. This results in cell multiplication and elongation which we recognize as "growth." Leaves also have another function, namely, the temporary storage of the food manufactured during the process of photosynthesis. When an old leaf has stored food and this food is later used by the plant the leaf usually drops off.

It is important to understand plant structure to know how the raw materials which we supply in the nutrients are used. It is only natural that the plant cell—a unit which performs so many functions—should be rather complex in structure. The cell is not only the structural but

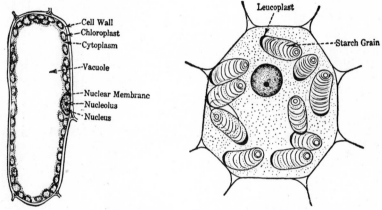

FIG. 24a. A typical plant cell highly magnified showing the various parts as mentioned in the text. This is from the palisade parenchyma of a leaf.

FIG. 24b. A highly magnified cell of *Pellionia* showing leucoplasts and contained starch grains. (Redrawn from Gager.)

also the functional unit of the plant. By this is meant that the innumerable plant cells which go to make up the entire plant are the actual structural units of the supporting skeleton, corresponding to bricks in a building, and at the same time are performing the growing and manufacturing operations which we have mentioned. We find by study under the microscope that the plant cell is divided into three parts: the cell walls, which vary considerably in thickness depending upon their position in the plant and their function; the protoplasm, which is the living part of the cell; and the vacuole, which is the cell sap. See Fig. 24a–b. Considering first the cell wall, we find it may be composed of a mixture of celluloses and other substances such as resins, gums, tannins, minerals, proteins, fats, oils, and coloring matter. The protoplasm or living part of the cell is a substance which has a viscous slimy consistency that is neither a true solid nor a true liquid and possesses a considerable power of cohesion. It is heavier than water but has no tendency to mix with it. It contains 80-90 per cent water, and about 7 per cent of dry matter as inorganic compounds such as chlorides, phosphates, sulfates, and carbonates of magnesium, potassium, sodium, calcium, and iron. The organic compounds representing the balance are chiefly proteins, carbohydrates, and fatty substances. Of these organic compounds about 40-50 per cent are nitrogenous. (See Miller, *Plant Physiology*, 1931 edition, page 16.) Nitrogen makes up 1-5 per cent of the total dry weight of plants, this percentage being exceeded by only three other elements, carbon, oxygen, and hydrogen. From this you will readily see that nitrogen in our nutrient solution is of vital importance.

By careful observation, we find that the protoplasm can be divided into three parts: the cytoplasm, or cell substance, usually containing food materials; the nucleus, or reproductive part of the cell; and the plastids, or the color-giving part of the cell. The *cytoplasm* is considered the less specialized portion of the protoplasm and forms the greater part of the bulk. The cytoplasm of one cell is connected with the cytoplasm of adjacent cells by minute pores in the cell-wall structure. The *nucleus* is the most important organ of the protoplasm, because, largely as the result of its behavior, cells reproduce and divide. The nucleus is a rounded portion of the protoplasm of the same structure as the cytoplasm but a little thicker in texture. It contains more nucleoprotein than the cytoplasm. The *plastids* are protoplasmic organs in the cell which perform certain physiological functions. They are divided into three classes: chloroplasts, which are green in color and vary in size; chromoplasts, which are red, yellow, or orange and are found primarily in the petals of flowers and in ripe fruits; and leucoplasts, which are colorless and can under certain circumstances change into either chloroplasts or chromoplasts. Leucoplasts transform carbohydrates into starches, and also, probably, they form oils and proteins. The chloroplasts, which were first mentioned, contain the all-important chlorophyll which is primarily concerned with the process of photosynthesis or the manufacture of carbohydrates from carbon dioxide and water.

As the plant cell begins to grow the protoplasm shows cavities of various sizes which become filled with water and materials in solution and in suspension. These cavities with their contents are called vacuoles. The vacuole or cell sap may contain the following materials: (1) water; (2) inorganic salts of sodium, potassium, magnesium, and calcium; (3) carbohydrates such as cane sugar, maltose, glucose, fructose, dextrose, and inulin; (4) nitrogenous compounds such as proteins, amino acids, and amides; (5) alkaloids such as atropin in belladonna, nicotine in tobacco, caffein in coffee, morphine in poppy, quinine in Peruvian bark tree, and many other of our well-known drugs; (6) fats and oils as in flax seed and castor beans; (7) resins as in conifers; (8) gum resins as in India rubber; (9) vegetable acids such as formic in stinging nettles, oxalic mostly in the form of calcium oxalate, malic in the apple, and citric in the lemon. It is these various materials in the cell sap which give our plants and fruit their definite characteristics. It is important that we know how these substances are held so that we will not change the characteristics of the fruit to its detriment. These substances can be varied by our nutrients, and we must see that the proper elements are available in sufficient quantities.

Storage cells of plants are living cells. The plant foods travel through the circulating system in the simpler forms such as sugar and are stored in the more complex form such as starches. The protoplasm will not allow them to travel in their storage forms. Sugar travels as glucose and fructose, fats as glycerine and fatty acids, and proteins travel as amino acids.

Transpiration, largely regulated by the amount of evaporation from the surface of the leaf, is very definitely related to this transportation of food and raw elements throughout the plant system. Reference to the highly magnified leaf section will show that the leaf surface is not smooth but is covered with tiny pores like the skin of the body. Most of these pores or stomata, as they are called, occur on the lower surface of the leaf. The stomata are simply intercellular openings each of which is surrounded by two guard cells. These guard cells control to a large extent the amount of evaporation from the plant. As long as the plant is well supplied with water the guard cells remain open. If the plant begins to wilt, the guard cells close and thus stop much of the evaporation. Besides evaporation, the stomata also regulate the intake of carbon dioxide and the outgo of oxygen during photosynthesis, as well as the reverse process, the intake of oxygen and the outgo of carbon dioxide in respiration. The term *stomata* may include the opening, the guard cells, and the adjacent cells surrounding the opening.

In this chapter we have attempted only to touch the high spots, mentioning briefly some of the processes with which we are concerned and how they bear on plant growth. The subject is extremely fascinating, and should you want to do any amount of experimenting and further research into nutrient growing you will probably wish to study it more intensely. See the Bibliography, page 127.

Chapter IX

ESSENTIAL ELEMENTS AND THEIR FUNCTION IN GROWTH

In the nutrient culture of plants we are concerned with fourteen essential elements. Although an analysis of a plant would probably show many more elements than this, it is doubtful whether all would play a definite role in the life of the plant. Many of these elements are undoubtedly present simply because they were in the soil and were carried into the plant along with others that were essential. The entire role played by each element is not known, but some of the important functions are. Thirteen of these essential elements are supplied from the soil or nutrient solution; the fourteenth is supplied by the carbon dioxide of the air. The fourteen elements are nitrogen, phosphorus, potassium, magnesium, calcium, sulfur, iron, manganese, zinc, copper, boron, hydrogen, oxygen, and carbon.

Nitrogen enters into the structure of the chlorophyll and the protoplasm of the plant. The protoplasm is the living part of a plant cell. Nitrogen is one of the constituents of proteins and amides. Amino acids are the intermediate state of the proteins. Proteins constitute a large part of the protoplasm. Nitrogen produces an abundance of growth and foliage; it slows up the ripening process and increases the length of the growing period. Excess of nitrogen produces a large weak growth. In the absence of nitrogen the leaves are stunted in growth and the foliage is yellow.

Phosphorus readily migrates from the older parts of the plant to the growing tips and the newly forming seeds. It is an important constituent of the nucleoproteins and is important in cell division and growth. Deficiency of phosphorus allows fats to accumulate in the cells, interferes with the transformation of starches into water-soluble carbohydrates, and often causes the cell walls to become thickened. This retards growth. Phosphorus is found mostly in the cell nuclei and especially in fruits and seeds.

Potassium has a function that is not entirely understood. We do know that carbohydrates are formed only in the presence of sufficient potassium. When potassium is deficient, starch is not manufactured and, even though sugar is furnished, proteins will not be formed. Plants grown in the absence of potassium produce much less dry matter than those in which it is sufficient. Potassium is found largely in the growing tips of the plant. There are indications that cells will not divide without sufficient amounts of this element. Strange as it may seem, growth does not entirely stop, for cell elongation continues, but cell division ceases. Potassium can be partly replaced by sodium, yet sodium is not an essential element in plant growth. Since potassium as found in the plant is readily soluble in water, it is apparent that this element is present in the form of inorganic compounds and as salts of organic acids. Potassium plays an important role in the formation of proteins and oils.

Calcium seems to have an important physiological role. It neutralizes acids that might otherwise become injurious in the plant cell.* There is a direct relation between the amount of calcium and the amount of nitrogen needed. When a large amount of nitrogen is used, a large amount of protein is formed; and when a large amount of protein is formed more oxalic and other acids are produced, which in turn requires more calcium to neutralize this excess acid. In the absence of calcium a large accumulation of starch occurs, and new cell walls are imperfectly formed. Calcium may reduce the toxicity of other elements such as sodium and magnesium. In respect to the amount required by the plant, calcium should be placed ahead of phosphorus as an important cell constituent. Calcium has not been considered to any great degree in fertilizer practices, mainly because few soils are deficient in calcium whereas many soils are deficient in phosphorus. However, in view of the quantity required by the plant, and of the speed with which physiological disorders develop from insufficient calcium, calcium should be ranked next to potassium and nitrogen as an important nutrient.

Magnesium is present in a plant in much smaller amounts than calcium. It is one of the constituents of chlorophyll, and when it is lacking there is a definite disturbance of the chlorophyll. If it is deficient, chlorosis (yellowing of the leaf) occurs. Magnesium acts as a carrier of phosphorus; it is found in the growing tips of the plant where phosphorus is most abundant. Magnesium is more abundant in the seeds and leaves than in the rest of the plant. It is necessary for the formation of vegetable oils.

---

* Calcium may cause precipitation of certain organic acids as distinguished from neutralization.

Sulfur, until very recently, has been underestimated in its value to the plant and the amount a plant can absorb. This misapprehension was due to the fact that much of the sulfur was lost by ash analysis. It is now estimated that a plant uses two-thirds as much sulfur as phosphorus, and some crops use even more. It occurs in plants chiefly in the form of proteins and sulfates. It is about evenly distributed throughout the different parts of the plant—leaves, stem, and roots. Sulfur is essential to the formation of proteins, and the higher the amount of sulfur in the protein of a certain plant the more sulfur that plant will require. Deficiency of sulfur restricts growth by limiting the formation of proteins. Sulfur increases root development. Though it is not a constituent of chlorophyll, the absence of sulfur will prevent the formation of chlorophyll. How it acts, no one knows, as yet. Little or no starch is formed if sulfur is deficient. Sulfates seem to increase the nitrogen content of plants, yet there is no direct relationship between sulfur and nitrogen. It is thought that sulfates increase the bacterial action in soils, thus releasing more nitrogen for the plant.

Iron is necessary for the growth and development of plants; it cannot be replaced by any other element. It is universally distributed throughout the plant but is hard to detect since it occurs in very small quantities and much of it is not water soluble. Plants deprived of iron do not produce chlorophyll and both the leaves and stems have a very yellowish color and are spoken of as being chlorotic. Strange as it may seem, iron is not a constituent of chlorophyll. Plants grown with sufficient iron and then suddenly deprived of it become chlorotic only on the new leaves, so that there is a marked contrast between the new and old foliage. Leaves deprived of iron begin to die at the top instead of from the bottom like plants lacking nitrogen, phosphorus, or potassium. This indicates that iron is somewhat immobile in plants and cannot readily move from one part of the plant to another part. Soils having a pH of 7 or above are sometimes deficient in iron because the high pH makes the iron less available. The acidity of a solution has much to do with the availability of the iron. A pH of 4.5 makes iron much more available than a pH of 6.5. (See reference to pH testing.) *

* One of the most serious factors in making iron unavailable is phosphate. The phosphate combines with the iron to form a very insoluble ferric phosphate, and that is one reason why it is desirable to keep the concentration of the phosphorus salt low in the nutrient solution.

Manganese is distributed throughout the entire plant. The amount found depends largely upon the amount available; if large quantities are available, a greater amount is found in the plant. Manganese is found in seeds in about equal amounts with iron. Enough manganese is stored up in the seed of some plants to supply them throughout the entire growing period. Plants deprived of manganese lack chlorophyll development and will not produce seed. Manganese also makes plants more resistant to disease. (Gray speck disease of oats is caused by manganese deficiency.) It is believed that manganese helps the plant to assimilate other elements. Manganese may cause the plant to assimilate more calcium, which, in turn, may make the iron unavailable and cause a chlorotic condition.

Boron is necessary for plant growth, but if used in any but the smallest quantities it is toxic. Legumes require a larger quantity than other crops because boron seems to help in the nitrogen-fixing process. Plants that require boron cannot be satisfied with any other element. Boron acts in a nutritive way and is necessary throughout the life of the plant. If boron is deficient the cells at the growing tip cease to divide. The bases of young leaves begin to die after injury, caused by a deficiency of this element.

Zinc is present in plants, but its role is not well known. Plants grown in the absence of zinc have all the appearance of plants grown in very poor soil. Zinc is a catalyst and speeds up reactions; it should be used very carefully. (As little as 1 ppm. may be toxic to some plants.)

Carbon, oxygen, and *hydrogen* enter into all organic compounds in the plant and compose more than 95 per cent of its dry weight. The carbon is obtained from the air as carbon dioxide. Hydrogen and most of the oxygen enter as water, although some oxygen is taken in from the air.

Copper is not so important as iron, but it serves much the same purpose. It acts as a catalytic agent. It is a carrier of oxygen and helps speed up respiration.

Chapter X

TESTING NUTRIENT SOLUTIONS

Much of your success with nutrient-solution culture depends upon your accuracy in testing the nutrient solution and in making an occasional leaf tissue test. The method of colorimetric analysis has been perfected to the point where it is extremely accurate as a quantitative test for various elements. Although this method will probably never take the place of the regular quantitative process of analyzing compounds, it does adapt itself to a number of procedures where speed of analysis is important and absolute accuracy is not necessary. Colorimetric analysis is the method used in testing nutrient solutions, and the exact procedure has been adapted from the many "quick-test" soil kits that have been developed. If you are already using a rapid-test soil kit in your greenhouse work, the procedure can be adapted to solution testing; if you are not using such tests on your greenhouse soils we suggest that when you get your solution test kit you use it also in testing your soils.

A Simple Laboratory

To take care of testing your solutions properly you should set up a small laboratory. It need not be elaborate or take a great deal of space. It can be any small room which is well lighted (preferably with a good north light), and it should have running water available. You should also install a large (150-watt) blue glass electric light to use on dark days. This should be placed so that you can make your readings in a strong light. A small work table should be constructed, of a height to allow the worker to stand. This bench should be covered with a good grade of linoleum for ease in keeping it clean. At the back edge of this bench, placed so that it does not interfere with the light from the window, a small shelf should be built to hold the various bottles of chemicals and reagents. Also at a height of 6 feet, build a shelf large enough and strong enough to hold a 5-gallon bottle of distilled water. By placing the bottle at this height it is easy to siphon the water out with a piece of small rubber tubing which can be left permanently attached and closed with an ordinary clamp.

In addition to the supplies contained in the regular test kit, you will need a glass cylinder graduate of 100-cc. capacity, a glass wash bottle of 500-cc. capacity, two or three pipettes of 10-cc. capacity graduated in cubic centimeters, several test-tube racks, a small white porcelain test plate with twelve cavities, several beakers and flasks (each about 100-cc. capacity), a number of extra test tubes or small vials, several extra funnel tubes, about 5 feet of ¼-inch rubber tubing, and a small hose clamp. With any of the standard test kits you will probably get about a dozen small test tubes and the same number of funnel tubes, a small metal spoon for measuring definite quantities of powders or soil, a package of small filter papers to use with the funnel tubes, one large pipette (10-cc.), and several small bottles of various reagents with full directions for use.* These small bottles of reagents can be replenished by purchasing larger, more economical sizes and refilling the smaller bottles from time to time. As the prepared reagents are quite inexpensive, we recommend that you do not try to mix your own.

To mix your own reagents you need an extremely accurate balance sensitive to 0.001 gram, a number of different chemicals, and a great deal of skill.

Laboratory Technic. The most important points in laboratory technic are discussed next for those who have not had actual experience. We cannot emphasize too strongly the value of keeping your laboratory clean and the necessity of keeping the test tubes and other apparatus absolutely immaculate. Do not allow loose chemicals to be scattered about the laboratory. Keep them in closed glass bottles or jars at all times. As only very small quantities of solutions are required for the tests we recommend, even a small amount too much or a few grains of pure chemical will spoil their accuracy. Ordinary tap water contains many impurities, and for that reason it should be used only in preliminary washing of flasks, test tubes, and pipettes. Each instrument should have a final rinsing with distilled water. All measuring of quantities should be *exact*. As an example, in using the pipette, the tip of this tube is inserted below the surface of the liquid to be measured, suction is applied to the pipette, and the liquid rises in the tube. (CAUTION: Keep the tip of the pipette below the surface of the liquid or you will draw it into your mouth.) You should bring

---

* You will find it more convenient to have several small medicine droppers graduated in 0.1 cc. than to use the tiny pipette which is often furnished.

Fig. 25. An ideal laboratory arrangement. Can be made much simpler and less expensive than this but should carry out the general ideas portrayed and should include a sink.

the level of the liquid to a point about 1 inch above the mark indicating the quantity you want to measure and then quickly put the forefinger over the upper end of the tube. This will hold the liquid in the tube and the pipette can be removed from the solution. By releasing the pressure with the forefinger the liquid will flow out of the pipette as slowly as one drop at a time. You will notice that the surface of the liquid in the tube is concave, and the reading should be taken at the bottom of this curve, to be accurate. A small amount of liquid will remain in the constricted tip of the tube, but the graduations are so marked that, when all the liquid that will run out naturally without blowing into or shaking the pipette has drained from the tube, you will have a full measure.

GENERAL LABORATORY DIRECTIONS

The following general directions for manipulation should be closely followed:

1. Every bottle should have a definite place on the side shelf and should be kept in its place.

2. Use the exact amount of material specified.

3. If you spill some chemical or reagent, do not try to return it to the bottle, as you might contaminate the remainder. Throw it away.

4. When you remove the stopper of a reagent bottle, do not lay it on the bench. Hold it between the first and second fingers, and, when you are through using it, replace it immediately in the proper bottle.

5. Each time you measure a liquid with the pipette, rinse it with distilled water before measuring a different liquid.

6. Before you put a reagent or solution into the test tube, rinse the tube with distilled water, and shake out the excess water.

7. One of the tests calls for the use of a clean tin stirring rod. Before using this tin rod, scrape it thoroughly with a knife so that it is absolutely clean and shiny. Do not use it to stir more than two or three solutions without again scraping it to give it a shiny surface.

8. Some of the tests call for cork stoppers in the tubes so that the solution can be shaken to get thorough distribution of the reagent and to hurry the reaction. Always wash these corks before using them, and rinse with distilled water.

9. One of the tests calls for examination of the tested solution by looking through it at light and heavy black lines. This must be done in a strong light to get accurate results. The intensity of this light should be uniform at all times. Always use a bulb of the same wattage and have it at the same distance from your work.

10. When you finish with your testing, wash everything thoroughly with tap water, using a test-tube brush on the small vials if necessary. Then put everything away perfectly clean and in its proper place.

Rapid-Test Kits

A great many rapid-test kits designed to test soils in the laboratory and in the field are on the market. We know of no kit that has been designed primarily for testing nutrient solutions, but almost any one of the soil kits can be adapted to the purpose. We have used several different kits and have finally adopted a testing procedure which we believe incorporates the best features and most accurate tests of these various kits. As stated above, though it is possible for the grower to prepare his own reagents, we believe it to be more practical to purchase them ready for use.* Nevertheless, we give you below the method of preparing some of these reagent solutions for those who want to try making their own.

Although we acknowledge that there are many good test kits, we prefer the Purdue nitrate test for leaf tissue and the Purdue acidity tests for determining the relative acidity of the solution. In making tests of the *solution* for potassium, nitrogen, magnesium, and phosphorus, we use the Urbana Laboratory Kit. We think this selection of tests much simpler to run, and we find that they are highly accurate. Directions for preparing the reagents used in making what we will call the Purdue acidity test and the Purdue nitrate test are given below. The first three reagents are used in the acidity test and give very satisfactory results if the acidity range is between pH 3.8 and pH 7.5, which is sufficient for our purpose. Relative acidity or alkalinity may be designated in this way. If the solution shows a pH 8-9 it is medium alkaline. If it shows pH 7-8 it is slightly alkaline, and if it shows pH 7 it is neutral. Likewise, pH 6-7 indicates a slightly acid solution, pH 5-6 a medium acid solution, and pH 4-5 a very acid solution. Solutions more acid than pH 4 or more alkaline than pH 9 usually are not suitable for crop production. If you are making your pH tests regularly there will be no reason to let the solution reach such dangerous points. Correct it by adding an acid or lye as necessary, as soon as the pH is out of line.

Reagents for Testing Relative Acidity

Indicator 1. Dissolve 0.04 gram of bromothymol blue powder in 5 cc. of 95 per cent ethyl alcohol; add 95 cc. of distilled water. Using a 0.2 normal solution of sodium hydroxide, add it drop by drop until

* The acidity reagents may be purchased from the Agronomy Department, Purdue University, Lafayette, Indiana, or the LaMotte Chemical Company, Baltimore, Maryland.

the color of this solution becomes a yellowish green (indicating an acidity of pH 6.6). The reagent is now ready for use and has a range effective from pH 5.8 to 7.5. Its use will be explained later.

Indicator 2. Dissolve 0.04 gram of bromocresol green powder in 5 cc. of 95 per cent ethyl alcohol; add 95 cc. of distilled water. In the same way as above, add 0.2 normal solution of sodium hydroxide drop by drop until the color of this indicator is brought to a yellowish green (indicating an acidity of pH 4.6). This indicator has an effective range from pH 3.8 to 5.5.

Special Indicator. Dissolve 0.04 gram of chlorophenol red in 5 cc. of 95 per cent ethyl alcohol; add 95 cc. of distilled water. Adjust it in the same way, adding 0.2 normal solution of sodium hydroxide drop by drop until the color becomes a reddish orange (indicating an acidity of pH 5.6). The range of this indicator is pH 4.8 to 6.2.

When these reagents are bought ready prepared, a color chart accompanies them which enables you to check accurately until you have the various colors thoroughly established in your mind.

To test the acidity of the nutrient solution, use the white porcelain test plate. Put a few drops of the solution to be tested in three of these depressions. To one of them add one or two drops of indicator 1, to another add one or two drops of indicator 2, and to the third add one or two drops of the special indicator. If indicator 1 gives a distinct blue color it indicates that the solution is pH 7.4 or above. If the color is bluish-green the pH is 7.0, if the color is yellowish-green the pH is 6.6, if the color is greenish-yellow the pH is 6.2, and if the color is bright yellow the pH is 5.8 or below.

If we got a bright yellow color with indicator 1, then we refer to the test with indicator 2 and find that a distinct blue color indicates a pH of 5.4 or above. A bluish-green color indicates a pH of 5.0, yellowish-green indicates pH 4.6, a greenish-yellow pH 4.2, and a bright yellow pH 3.8 or less. Since we do not want the solution to be lower than pH 3.8 we do not need to carry this test lower but simply adjust the acidity so that it is at the right point.

If with our first test using indicator 1 we find that the pH falls somewhere beween 5.0 and 6.0 and wish to get the reading more accurately we refer to the test using the special indicator.* If with this indicator the color is a distinct red, the pH is 6.1 or above. A reddish-orange color indicates pH 5.8, an orange color indicates pH 5.5, a yellowish-orange pH 5.2, and a distinct yellow pH 4.9 or below. Other

* It is not necessary to check the acidity as accurately as is done with the special indicator, so we seldom use it.

colorimetric tests are available which cover a greater range of acidity but these three are sufficient for our purpose. If you find that the nutrient solution is too acid, correct it by adding carefully a little lye to the tank and again testing until you have the acidity right. If the solution is too alkaline, add a little sulfuric acid slowly to the tank until the acidity is correct. After correcting the acidity stir the solution thoroughly and then retest to be sure it is right.

REAGENT FOR NITRATE TEST (PURDUE)

Reagent 1. Dissolve 1 gram of diphenylamine in 100 cc. of concentrated sulfuric acid. This solution is very corrosive. (It should be kept in a glass-stoppered bottle. Avoid getting it on clothes or hands.) If this reagent has turned pink or blue by aging it should be discarded as it is then no good for testing.

We prefer this test for determining nitrogen fixation in foliage. We are not particularly concerned with the amount of nitrogen as we do not want *any* to appear in the test. To make the foliage test we again use the white porcelain test plate. (Wash plate thoroughly and rinse with distilled water.) Scrape or crush the petiole of a young leaf, getting some of the bruised tissue into the depression. Add a drop or two of the above reagent. A light blue color indicates that nitrogen is being stored in the leaf; a dark blue color indicates that a great deal of nitrogen is being stored. Nitrogen should never be present in rose foliage, and if it is found the solution contains too much nitrogen. It is not very practical to try to remove this excess nitrogen from the solution, so we adjust it by being careful not to add any salt supplying nitrogen until the solution has been further depleted. An excess of nitrogen can be counteracted by increasing the concentration of potassium as shown on the nitrogen-potassium chart. Carnation foliage will always give a nitrogen test, but this apparently is not important.

For making the other solution tests we prefer the kit sold by the Urbana Laboratories. This kit has a very accurate nitrogen test. Most of the tests give practically quantitative results. The set was primarily designed for testing soils, but Professor Bray and Dr. Whiting have worked out a procedure especially for inclusion in this book which adapts all the technic to accurate testing of nutrient solutions. It is possible that a similar procedure could be applied to other test kits which you might prefer to use. All nutrient solutions contain a much higher concentration of nutrient salts than you will find in ordinary soils, and for that reason the nutrient solution must be diluted a great deal in order to bring the concentration within the reading range of the methods used and secure an accurate reading. All the reagents in this test kit have trade names which indicate the use for which they are intended. If you purchase this test kit you receive specific instructions for testing soils, but we are not repeating those directions here since we are interested in nutrient solutions. One important point to remember in the summer is that when testing the solution for potassium both the reagent and the solution should be lower than 90° F. If the room in which you are testing is warmer than this, cool the reagent and the solution by running cool tap water over the outside of the tubes or bottles.

Urbana Laboratories Tests

The greenhouse and soil tests, prepared by the Urbana Laboratories, Urbana, Illinois, can be used to determine the concentration of and to adjust the important plant food elements in tank culture solutions. The procedure is, in each case, to test the solution after it has been used by the plants, at intervals of once a week or oftener for certain elements (we test twice a week), or at longer intervals for those elements used less rapidly by the plants. The tests will give an approximately correct value in parts per million (ppm.) of the element in question. The difference between the parts per million (ppm.) found in the used culture solution and the parts per million originally present is the amount in parts per million which must be added to restore the solution to its original strength. The tests as presented here serve as guides for controlling the concentration of culture solutions in coarse gravel and in cinders. These same tests and others available from the Urbana Laboratories are valuable for use on greenhouse soils. We usually test for nitrogen, potassium, and phosphorus twice a week and for magnesium only once every week or two. We seldom test for calcium as we know we have enough because we supply both nitrogen and phosphorus by means of calcium salts. We test for iron twice a week just as a check but add iron by sprinkling on the benches as explained before, regardless of whether we get a test for iron. Roses particularly seem to need a great deal of iron in small quantities added frequently. If you are having any difficulties you may find it advisable to test your solution more often.

When you prepared your original nutrient solution for the tanks, we told you to put aside in a gallon bottle some of this solution as you know exactly the concentration of the various salts you incorporated in that solution. Let us take for example a typical solution such as you might start with in the summer.

Salt Used	Element	PPM.
$Ca(NO_3)_2$	N	450
K_2SO_4	K	100
$CaH_4(PO_4)_2$	P	70
$MgSO_4$	Mg	60

As this solution has not been used by the plants the concentration remains constant and by using it in proper dilution we always have a check test to compare with the depleted solution we are testing. Thus we know approximately how much of each salt should be added to bring the used solution to the proper concentration. The terms "original solution," "standard solution," and "unused solution" refer to the solution used to fill the tank for the first time. The terms "depleted solution" and "used solution" refer to the solution after it has been fed to the plants.

REAGENTS FOR NITRATE TEST (URBANA LABORATORIES)

Mor-Les-Nitrate Reagent 1 (Powder)
Mor-Les-Nitrate Reagent 2
Mor-Les-Nitrate Reagent 3

The sensitivity of the nitrate test makes it necessary to dilute the culture solution unless most of the nitrates have been used from the solution by the plant. If you have an approximate idea of the parts per million remaining in the solution, the dilutions listed below will tell you how to prepare your solution for testing. If you do not know the approximate concentration you will have to try several different dilutions until you arrive at an approximate test corresponding to the color test shown by your standard solution.

How to Make the Test. If the culture solution after its use by the plants contains approximately the amount shown in the first column, dilute it the number of times shown in the second column by the method shown in the third column.

PPM.	Times to Dilute	Procedure
50	10	To 1 cc. solution add distilled water to make 10 cc.
100	20	To 1 cc. solution add distilled water to make 20 cc.
200	40	To 1 cc. solution add distilled water to make 40 cc.
400	80	To 1 cc. solution add distilled water to make 80 cc.

If when making the test the above dilutions show too deep a color (the color should be pink, not deep red), a greater dilution should be used. To perform the nitrate test, put 1 cc. of this diluted solution in one of the small flat-bottom test tubes, add 1 small spoonful of reagent 1 (powder), then add enough reagent 2 to fill the vial about three-quarters full, insert a clean cork and shake for about 15 or 20 seconds, remove cork, and add 1 cc. of reagent 3. The pink color will begin to develop immediately. Compare this color with those shown on the nitrate color chart to find the pounds per acre. The soil test reading chart can be changed from pounds per acre to parts per million by the following table:

Color of solution corresponds to color on chart showing:	Parts per million (ppm.) of nitrogen in the diluted solution:
10 lb. per acre	1 ppm.
20 lb. per acre	3 ppm.
30 lb. per acre	5 ppm.
40 lb. per acre	7 ppm.

Intermediate colors not shown on chart:

15 lb. per acre	2 ppm.
25 lb. per acre	4 ppm.

If a 30 lb. per acre reading is obtained, then there are 5 ppm. of nitrogen in the diluted solution, and if you diluted the solution 10 times, multiply this reading of 5 ppm. by 10, which gives 50 ppm. of nitrogen in the used solution before diluting. If a reading of 5 ppm. is obtained and you diluted the solution 20 times before testing, then multiply 5 ppm. by 20 and you have 100 ppm. of nitrogen in the used solution before diluting.

Suppose you find from this test that your solution in the tank has 100 ppm. of nitrogen and at the time of year you are testing it should have 250 ppm. By referring to the table which you previously made showing the number of grams of each salt to add to the tank to make 1 ppm. you can determine the number of grams to add to the tank to make up this deficiency of 150 ppm. by multiplying the number of grams shown in the table by 150. (The table referred to throughout this chapter in determining the amount of salts to add is the table which you calculate showing the number of grams required to give 1 ppm. An example of such a table is shown on page 55, and blank pages for recording such a table for each of your tanks are supplied at the end of the book.) Make a notation of this amount of nitrogen salt to be added, and continue testing for the other elements. Then weigh all your chemicals and add them at one time.

Another method of running the nitrate test, and one which we prefer, uses the standard solution as a check test. Dilute the standard solution as follows. (CAUTION: In making all your tests be sure to rinse pipette, graduate, and all other instruments with distilled water before using them with a different solution or reagent. Absolute cleanliness is necessary.) With the pipette measure 1 cc. of the unused solution (the bottle of solution you put aside when you originally filled the tank) and put it in the 100-cc. graduate; add enough distilled water to make 80 cc. of dilute solution. (This dilutes the original solution 80 times.)

Rinse the pipette; measure 1 cc. of this diluted solution, and put it in one of the small flat-bottomed vials. Pour the remainder of the diluted solution out of the graduate, rinse it, and prepare a second specimen diluting 1 cc. of the unused solution 40 times by adding enough water to make 40 cc. Take 1 cc. of this diluted solution and put it in a second small vial. Prepare a third specimen by diluting 1 cc. of the unused solution 20 times, and then put 1 cc. of this diluted solution in a small vial. You now have three specimens of this original unused solution and should perform the nitrate test on each of them as before. This will give you three different intensities of color because there are three different concentrations of nitrogen in the three specimens.

You are now ready to work with the solution which has been used by the plants. Prepare a dilute specimen of this solution in the same manner as above, using 1 cc. and diluting 20 times by adding enough water to make 20 cc. Using 1 cc. of this dilute solution, perform the nitrate test in the usual way. The color which develops should be lighter than one of the three tests of the diluted unused solution, and that one should be selected for comparison.

The next step is to build up the concentration of the used solution until it exactly matches the color of your selected specimen. Since you diluted 1 cc. of this used solution to 20 cc. and the color developed is lighter than the selected specimen, this indicates that there are fewer parts per million in the used solution than in the diluted unused solution. Therefore we build up the concentration of this used solution by using more than 1 cc. in our test. We now try 1.2 cc. diluted to 20 cc. and perform the test. If this still is too light we try again, using 1.3 cc. diluted to 20 cc.; or if it was too dark we try 1.1 cc. diluted to 20 cc. Let us assume that the trial with 1.3 cc. diluted to 20 cc. and tested did match the selected specimen as to color. We know from our formula that the original unused solution had 450 ppm. of nitrogen.

Then if our used solution diluted 1 to 20 matched with the unused solution diluted 1 to 80, we divide this original 450 ppm. by 4, or if it
matched with the 1 to 40 dilution which is twice the dilution of the
used solution we divide by 2, or if it matched with the 1 to 20 dilution
we use the 450 ppm. in our calculation because the two solutions we
are comparing are of the same dilution. If in our test it required 1.3 cc.
diluted to 20 cc. to match the standard solution diluted 1 to 40, we
make this calculation to find the parts per million in the used tank
solution.

$$\frac{1 \text{ cc. of original solution has known ppm.}}{\text{Dilution of original solution}} = \frac{1.3 \text{ cc. used solution unknown ppm.}}{\text{Dilution of used solution}}$$

Substituting:

$$\frac{450}{40} = \frac{1.3x}{20}$$

Simplifying:

$$(40 \times 1.3) = 52x = 9,000 = (450 \times 20)$$
$$x = 173$$

Solving for x, we find that there are 173 ppm. in our used tank
solution. If at this time of year we want to carry 200 ppm. in the
tank solution, there is a deficiency of 27 ppm. $(200 - 173 = 27)$. Referring to the table showing the number of grams of calcium nitrate to
add to the tank for 1 ppm. we multiply that number of grams by 27
and add it to the tank.

As you become familiar with testing solutions you will soon learn
by the color developed in the used solution approximately how many
parts per million are deficient and you will be able to omit some of
these steps.

REAGENT FOR PHOSPHORUS TEST (URBANA LABORATORIES)
Hi-Lo-Fosfate Solution H
Phosphate color chart
Tin rod

To test the solution for phosphorus we take a portion of the original
solution used in the tank as a standard. Dilute this standard, if the
culture solution is being maintained around 80 ppm. of phosphorus, by
diluting 4 cc. of this original unused solution to 80 cc. with distilled
water. Measure out 1 cc. of this diluted solution to use as a check
test; add 1 cc. of Hi-Lo-Fosfate Solution H, and stir with the tin rod.
The blue color obtained should be about the same as between the
medium to high range on the phosphate color chart. To test the used
solution, take 4 cc. of the solution which the plant has used and dilute

to 40 cc. Measure out 1 cc. of this diluted solution, and add 1 cc. of Hi-Lo-Fosfate Solution H. Develop the color by stirring with the tin rod. Compare this color with that developed in the diluted unused solution. If the color developed in the used solution specimen is darker than the check test specimen, then more than half of the original amount of phosphorus remains in the used solution; if the color is lighter than the check test specimen, then more than half of the phosphorus has been used by the plants. Usually the color developed in the used solution specimen will be darker than that developed in the check test specimen. Continue to dilute the used solution specimen until its color matches the color of the check test specimen. (This color should be the medium plus shown on the color chart.)

The following table indicates the calculation to determine the parts per million in the used solution:

If 4 cc. of used solution diluted to 100 cc. gives medium plus color, then the solution contains 100 ppm.

If 4 cc. of used solution diluted to 50 cc. gives medium plus color, then the solution contains 50 ppm.

If 4 cc. of used solution diluted to 25 cc. gives medium plus color, then the solution contains 25 ppm.

From the above you will notice that the number of cubic centimeters of distilled water necessary to bring the color to the same value as the check test specimen or to medium plus on the color chart also indicates the number of parts per million of phosphorus remaining in the used solution. If the test shows that the solution after being used by the plants contains 40 ppm. and it should have 70 ppm., the difference or 30 ppm. can be made up by referring to the table and calculating the number of grams to add in the same way as with the nitrate test. Whatever number of parts per million at which you carry your phosphorus indicates the dilution for your check test specimen, and the used solution specimen should be diluted to give twice this concentration by diluting it only half as much as the check test specimen; i.e., if you are carrying 70 ppm. of phosphorus in your tank solution then dilute 4 cc. of the standard solution to 70 cc. and dilute 4 cc. of the used solution to 35 cc., or if you are carrying 100 ppm. of phosphorus in the tank solution then dilute 4 cc. of the standard solution to 100 cc. and dilute 4 cc. of the used solution to 50 cc.

REAGENT FOR POTASH TEST (URBANA LABORATORIES)
Lac-Hi-Potash Reagent B
Lac-Hi-Potash Reagent C
Scale for potassium test

If ammonium salts have been used to supply nitrogen in the solution culture, the potash test will not give an exact value until the ammonia has been converted to nitrates. It is for this reason that we prefer to use some other salt such as calcium nitrate, $Ca(NO_3)_2$, to furnish the nitrogen as this cannot possibly cause any interference with the potassium test.

We do not use a standard solution in testing for potassium but simply develop the test with the solution that has been used by the plants. It is important to follow carefully the procedure as given. With this test we use the small medicine droppers that are marked in 0.1 cc. because we use very small quantities of reagent and tested solution. First measure with the pipette 1 cc. of the solution that has been used by the plants, and place it in one of the small flat-bottom test vials. To this add 3 drops of Lac-Hi-Potash Reagent B (add 4 drops if the reagent is more than three months old). Add this reagent very gently with one of the medicine droppers, rotating the vial or shaking it slightly to mix the solutions. Then carefully add 1 cc. of Lac-Hi-Potash Reagent C, making sure that it is allowed to trickle slowly down the side of the inclined vial drop by drop so that very little mixing takes place. If this is done carefully the two liquids should be separated by a ring. Next shake the vial very gently by rotating so that the two liquids mix slowly and thoroughly, and you will find that a fine precipitate forms. Next take a perfectly clean flat-bottom vial and hold it 1 cm. (about half an inch) above the black lines on the test chart, having a strong light from a north window or a 150-watt light placed within a foot of the tube as a source of light. Once you become accustomed to a certain intensity of light always use the same kind. By means of the medicine dropper calibrated in 0.1 cc. measure the suspension of developed precipitate into the vial until the thin lines are just obscured. Check this by moving the vial over the heavy dark lines. They should be readily visible.

You should fix the focus of the eye on the chart and not on the top of the solution. Without changing the focus of the eye, move the tube back over the thin lines and see if they are still obscured. If not, add a drop more and again check. Do this until the thin lines are obscured and yet the heavy lines are still visible. It should require at least 1 cc. of the turbid solution to obscure the thin lines; if it does not, this indicates that the potassium is too concentrated in the testing specimen so we must dilute the solution more. When less than 1 cc. of precipitate is required to obscure the thin lines, the test should be run again, using 1 cc. of the used solution diluted with 1 cc. of distilled water. Take 1 cc. of this mixture and run the test carefully as before. The precipitate this time should be much lighter, and it should require at least 1 cc. to obscure the thin lines. Assuming that it took 1.6 cc. of precipitate to obscure the lines, we refer to the table below and read directly the parts per million of potassium in the solution. If the solution has been diluted one-half, be sure to multiply the results by 2 to make up for this dilution. In this table we show in the third column the pounds of potassium per acre in case you want to use the test kit on your greenhouse soils.

CC. of Precipitate to Obscure Lines	PPM. of Potassium in Used Solution	Pounds per Acre of Potassium
1.0	75	300
1.1	68	270
1.2	62	250
1.3	57	230
1.4	53	213
1.5	50	200
1.6	46	184
1.7	44	176
1.8	42	168
1.9	40	160
2.0	38	150
2.1	36	144
2.2	34	136
2.3	33	132
2.4	31	126
2.5	30	120
2.6	29	116
2.7	28	111
2.8	26	105
2.9	25	100
3.0	24	96
3.5	19	75
4.0	15	60
4.5	12	50

If we find, after making any calculations to correct for dilution of the solution, that there are only 46 ppm. of potassium and we need 70 ppm., the deficiency of 24 ppm. is made up by adding the number of grams of the potassium salt found by referring to the table we compiled when we mixed our solution. This table shows the number of grams needed to supply 1 ppm., and this, multiplied by 24, indicates the amount to add to the tank.

REAGENTS FOR CALCIUM TEST (URBANA LABORATORIES)
Calcium Reagent A
Scale same as used for potassium test

FIG. 26. Large concrete tank constructed under benches. Note that any pipes such as purlins or ventilating posts (particularly if galvanized), if they are in contact with the solution, must be painted with Korite. The pump pit in this installation is behind the wall at the far end. This tank holds 3,000 gallons (12,000 liters.)

As stated before, we seldom test for calcium as we know there is enough since we supply both nitrogen and phosphorus by means of calcium salts. Plants will stand as much as 3,000 ppm. of calcium, and it would be unusual if you ever had that much. However, we give below the method of testing for calcium in case you want to use it.

Measure in the pipette 2 cc. of the solution that has been used by the plants and put it in one of the small flat-bottom vials. Add 2 cc. of calcium reagent A, let stand 1 minute, and then immediately read the turbidity in the same way the potassium test is read, i.e., by taking a clean flat-bottom vial, using the dropper calibrated in 0.1 cc., drop in enough to obscure the thin lines but not the heavy lines. Note how many 0.1 cc. were required, and read the parts per million direct from the chart below. (If the solution has more than 1,500 ppm. it must be diluted to bring it within the range of this turbidity chart.)

CC. Necessary to Obscure Thin Lines	PPM. of Calcium in the Solution	CC. Necessary to Obscure Thin Lines	PPM. of Calcium in the Solution
0.5	1,500	1.5	250
0.6	1,000	2.0	200
0.7	600	2.5	160
0.8	450	3.0	130
0.9	380	3.5	110
1.0	320		

If you should find that your solution does need more calcium, again calculate the deficiency, refer to the table showing the number of grams to make 1 ppm., and add the correct amount to the tank.

MAGNESIUM TEST REAGENTS (URBANA LABORATORIES)
Magnesium Reagent 1
Magnesium Reagent 2

To make the magnesium test we usually take a standard solution as a check test. Take 1 cc. of the original stock tank solution. Add 1 drop of magnesium reagent 1; add 1 drop of magnesium reagent 2. Next take 1 cc. of the solution which has been used by the plants and develop the test in the same way, adding a drop of each reagent. If the standard solution gives a test much darker than the used solution test, determine the amount of magnesium to add by diluting the standard solution to various concentrations and testing until the same color is reached in the standard solution that we have in the used solution. Then, on the basis of percentage of dilution, determine the amount of the magnesium salt to add. For example, if to make the colors match we had to dilute as shown below, then the percentage of magnesium shown has been used from the solution by the plants. Colors match when:

1 cc. unused solution plus 1 cc. distilled water shows ½ magnesium has been used

1 cc. unused solution plus ½ cc. distilled water shows ⅓ magnesium has been used

1 cc. unused solution plus 2 cc. distilled water shows ⅔ magnesium has been used

1 cc. unused solution plus 3 cc. distilled water shows ¾ magnesium has been used

1 cc. unused solution plus 4 cc. distilled water shows ⅘ magnesium has been used

Refer to the table we made up when we first filled the tank, and add the number of grams necessary to bring the concentration back to the original strength. Unless there is a great difference between the color developed in the used solution and the color developed in the original stock solution, we do not go to the trouble of calculating the exact amount of magnesium. We ordinarily assume that, if the solution which has been used by the plants when tested shows a slight blue or purple color or a blue precipitate, enough magnesium is present in the solution. If at the same time a slight pink color is present there is not too much magnesium in the solution. (This test is not sensitive enough for less than 10-15 ppm.)

REAGENTS FOR THE IRON TEST (URBANA LABORATORIES)
Ammonium Thiocyanate, 20% Solution
Hydrochloric Acid Diluted 1-1 with Distilled Water

To test for iron, measure 10 cc. of the solution to be tested, add 0.5 cc. of 1-1 HCl (hydrochloric acid), add 0.5 cc. of the ammonium thiocyanate (NH_4SCN), and check with a known standard. This test gives a pink to reddish color, depending upon the amount of iron present in the solution. If any color shows it probably indicates that enough iron is present, but in any event we always add iron direct to the benches as explained in Chapter VII as we find that if the plants are showing iron deficiency they need small quantities of iron at frequent intervals.

FOLIAGE TESTING

Leaf testing is important to verify certain deficiency symptoms or excesses that may be present. We explained a simple leaf tissue test for nitrogen, but to test for phosphorus or potassium the procedure is different. Phosphorus and potassium should always be present in large quantities in the leaves. To test for these elements in the young foliage or shoots, crush a few young leaves or other young plant parts thoroughly until they are well bruised and the juice shows clearly. Prepare a funnel tube by folding a small filter paper and inserting it in the top of the funnel tube. Place these crushed leaves in a test tube, and pour 10 cc. of reagent G_1 on them. Then filter the liquid into another test tube. Take 1 cc. of this filtrate and develop the *phosphate* test in the same manner as you did when using the tank solution. Take another sample of the filtrate (1 cc.) and develop the *potash* test, substituting the filtrate for the tank solution. These tests will tell you whether there is a quantity of phosphorus and potassium in the leaves. These elements should always be present.

The details we have given for making these tests may seem long and complicated as you read them. However, once you are familiar with the procedure, you will find that you do it almost automatically and that you can test solutions from several tanks in about 30 or 40 minutes.

As a final reminder, keep your testing equipment absolutely clean, measure accurately, follow instructions carefully, and remember that your success with nutrients depends largely upon the accuracy of your testing. Therefore it is essential that you have the best testing equipment that money can buy and that you learn to use it. You will find that it is quite simple once you become familiar with the various operations. Be sure to keep a record of your tests and any changes you make in your solution. This will help you the following year as you will be able to tell in advance just what changes in the formula will be needed at each period of the year.

CHAPTER XI

DIAGNOSING DEFICIENCY SYMPTOMS

The experienced commercial grower of greenhouse crops has learned over a long period of years how to tell from the condition of his plants just what they may need to give a maximum crop. This knowledge has been gained frequently through trial and error and at the expense of time and profits. Many growers guard this knowledge as a valuable trade secret. In the past the successful grower has been distinguished by the accuracy with which he recognizes difficulties and corrects them. Today, however, such valuable experimental work has been done by various investigators under reliably controlled conditions that this knowledge is available to anyone who will take the trouble to learn. Furthermore, research work has given an even better understanding of why plants have certain difficulties and what may best be done to correct them. Heretofore the grower knew that at a certain time of year his crop usually needed a mulch of manure. He did not always know why it needed this mulch or just what the mulch did for his crop. These accurate experiments have shed a great deal of light on the subject, and they are particularly helpful in nutrient-culture work.

These same symptoms that the grower of soil crops observed and acted upon apply to nutrient culture. The main difference is that we can use corrective measures that react much more quickly with nutrients than with soil and if weather or other conditions change rapidly we can readjust our solution almost instantly whereas with soil culture the process is much more expensive and the period of adjustment might take several weeks.

With the knowledge gained in the last chapter on testing the nutrient solution, we can tell a great deal about how our crop is progressing. This, together with the information given in this chapter on deficiency symptoms, will enable us to regulate scientifically the growth and productiveness of our plants.

DICHOTOMOUS KEY

It is very important that one learn to recognize nutrient deficiencies and excesses in the nutrient solution. By very careful observation, one can soon learn from the appearance of the crop just what ele-

106

ments need to be increased or decreased. One of the finest articles on this subject appeared under the name of L. C. Chadwick of Ohio State University, in the June, 1938, *Bulletin* published by Roses, Incorporated. With only minor changes in the numbering of his outline, we give you the article below:

KEY TO DEFICIENCY SYMPTOMS

Plants showing decreased growth, general on whole plant or localized. Insects and diseases absent.

I. *Effects general on whole plant or localized on older, lower leaves.*
   A. *Effects usually general on whole plant,* although often manifested by yellowing and dying of older leaves.
      1. *Foliage light green.* Growth stunted, stalks slender, and very few new breaks. Leaves small, lower ones lighter yellow than upper. Yellowing followed by a drying to a light brown color, usually very little dropping.
      This shows a deficiency of nitrogen.

      2. *Foliage dark green.* Delayed growth. Lower leaves sometimes yellow between veins but more often showing a tendency to develop a purplish coloration on the petiole. Leaves dropping early.
      This shows a deficiency of phosphorus.

   B. *Effects usually local on older, lower leaves.*
      1. *Lower leaves mottled, usually with necrotic spots near tips and margins.* Yellowing begins at margin and continues toward the center. Margins later become brown and curve under, and the older leaves drop off.
      This shows a deficiency of potassium.

      2. *Lower leaves chlorotic (yellow) but usually show no spotting until later stages.* Chlorosis begins at the leaf tip and progresses downward and inward, along the margins and between the veins. Leaf margins may curve upward or develop a puckering effect. (Seldom any deficiency in soils testing pH 5.5 or above.)
      This shows a deficiency of magnesium.

II. *Effects localized on new leaves.*
   A. *Terminal bud remaining alive.*
      1. *Leaves chlorotic (yellow) between the veins; veins remain green.*
         a. *Necrotic spots usually absent.* Extreme cases show drying of the margins of leaves and even die-back of the branches.
         This shows deficiency of iron.

    b. *Necrotic spots usually present* and scattered over the leaf surface. Checkered effect produced by small veins remaining green. Leaves shed. Young leaves may be etiolated. Poor bloom and weak growth.
This shows deficiency of manganese.

    2. *Leaves light green, veins lighter than adjoining interveinal areas.* Some necrotic spots appear. Little or no drying of older leaves.
This shows a deficiency of sulfur.

B. *Terminal bud usually dies.*
    1. *Breakdown at tip and margin of young leaves.* Young leaves often definitely hooked at tip.
This shows a deficiency of calcium.

    2. *Breakdown at base of young leaves.* Stems and petioles brittle.
This shows a deficiency of boron.

You will notice that the manner in which this table is made up requires only that you make a choice between two readily distinguishable symptoms and so leads you very directly to the answer to what is wrong.

DESCRIPTIVE KEYS

Another very fine article on this subject of deficiency symptoms was written by Arnold Wagner of Ohio State University. His findings are given below:

Nitrogen deficiency.
1. Poor growth. Plant shorter. Leaves small and stunted. Plant stunted. Short internodes.
2. Leaves turn yellowish-green and later entirely yellow.
3. Often veins are purplish.
4. Flowers smaller than normal.
5. Roots often more fully developed than tops.
6. Deficiency first occurs on lower leaves.

Phosphorus deficiency.
1. Early stages—a yellowing of the leaf margins.
2. Later stages—a gradual dying and dropping of leaves from bottom of plant.
3. Short growth.
4. Poor root system.

Potassium deficiency.
1. Yellowing of the leaf margins in the early stages followed later by a browning or dying of these yellow areas. Gives appearance of being scorched.
2. Later the leaves may become mottled between the veins.

PLATE III

This section of bench shows yield of "Golden Queen" tomatoes. Plants grew about 1 foot per week and were topped at 7 feet. Solution was pumped four times a day because of exposure to outside conditions. Solution was changed completely once each week to avoid the necessity of testing; discarded solution was used on flower beds. Solution without correction was always pH 5.6, which was right for these crops. Samples tested irregularly showed that just half of the chemicals had been used each week, so testing was not necessary. There were absolutely no weeds during the entire summer. Late in October tomatoes of large size were still ripening.

3. Plant more susceptible to insects and disease.
4. Deficiency occurs on lower leaves.

Iron deficiency.
1. Chlorosis, yellowing of the foliage.
2. Shows up first on tip of plant.
3. Reduced rate of growth.
4. In later stages there is a severe burning of the chlorotic leaves. It begins at the tips and margins and spreads inward.

Magnesium deficiency.
1. Stunted growth.
2. Chlorosis. The veins remain green while the area in between becomes yellow.
3. Puckering of the leaf.
4. This deficiency occurs first on the lower leaves of the plant.
5. Leaves small—petiole of leaf short.
6. Dead areas appear between the veins of the leaf in later stages. This burning appears rather suddenly (within a 24-hour period).
7. Blooming delayed. Flower color poor.

Calcium deficiency.
1. Practically all feeding roots killed.
2. Plant very stunted. Stops growing.
3. Tip of plant and tips of top leaves die back.

Manganese deficiency.
1. Chlorosis. Light yellowish-green between the veins with the remaining dark green. This can be distinguished from magnesium deficiency because manganese chlorosis first appears on the top of the plant whereas magnesium chlorosis first appears on the lower leaves.
2. Plants somewhat stunted.
3. Leaves tend to turn under at the margins.

Sulfur deficiency.
1. Deficiency appears first at top of plant.
2. Chlorosis. Sulfur chlorosis differs from all other types of chlorosis in that the veins become yellow while the rest of the leaf remains green.
3. Plant shorter.
4. Dead areas, purplish in color, appear at the base of the leaf.

From the January, 1938, issue of the *Fertilizer Review,* we quote part of an article relating to nutritional tests and deficiency symptoms. This article is a condensation of *Bulletin* 626 of the New Jersey Experiment Station and gives the results of research by M. A. Blake, G. T. Nightingale, and O. W. Davidson on apple trees. Since the descriptions of the various symptoms of nutritional deficiencies are given in great detail, we believe that they will be found very helpful. Although this experimental work was performed in connection with apple trees, the symptoms and corrective measures will no doubt apply equally well to most hardwooded crops.

DESCRIPTION OF DEFICIENCY SYMPTOMS

Nitrogen deficiency.

Leaves appear yellowish green.

New leaves are relatively small.

Red pigmentation may be present on veins and petioles.

Leaves assume an upright position and petioles form narrow angles with stem.

No conspicuous spotting or marking occurs on foliage.

Current growth of twigs and stems is short and slender.

Roots are slender with yellowing cortex on new growth.

Phosphorus deficiency.

Foliage abnormally dark green, especially the young leaves. When the deficiency is very severe, old leaves may appear somewhat mottled and lighter than younger leaves.

New leaves very small.

Both stems and leaves are usually highly pigmented with purplish-red, especially near the ends of the twigs.

Leaves have a leathery texture and form abnormally sharp angles with the stems.

Twigs are slender.

Potassium deficiency.

Twigs and stems are relatively slender, although linear growth may not be restricted appreciably.

Leaves are relatively small. If the deficiency has reached the stage at which "scorching" occurs, new leaves may be considerably smaller and thinner than normal.

Leaf-scorch appears first as a dull, dark purplish-red discoloration, involving the serrations of the leaves and extending inward slightly. This type of leaf injury differs distinctly from that produced by magnesium deficiency. The discolored areas enlarge very slowly in potassium deficiency and change from purplish-red to a dark brown without any intermediate whitish or gray stage.

Calcium deficiency.

Mature leaves have a normal, dark green color whereas young leaves may appear slightly yellowish-green.

Leaf size may or may not be affected significantly. On small trees the leaves may be abnormally small. On large trees the leaves may be normal in size except near the tips of the twigs, where they may be somewhat small.

Stem growth may be drastically restricted in length. Twigs may or may not be slender.

Roots usually show evidence of calcium deficiency in the growing medium long before any definite indication is shown by the top. The roots may become drastically stunted and may appear short and stubby with brownish tips. New roots may form profusely, but are usually short-lived.

There were no leaf lesions the first season but a discoloration developed the second season. This type of discoloration was unlike that in any of the other series. It was most prominent along the margins and extended about a quarter of an inch or more toward the midrib. The development of the discolored areas was preceded by a loss of chlorophyll. The veinlets became tinged with purple while the rest of the tissue in the affected areas changed gradually from greenish-yellow to dark brown. At this stage no purple was apparent in the discolored areas but it was usually very noticeable in the larger veins of the leaf.

Magnesium deficiency.

New leaves become thin and soft in texture as the deficiency progresses.

A slight mottling of the leaf develops quickly and is followed by blotching between the veins and along the margins. This discoloration and blotching appears first on the old leaves and progresses toward the stem tip.

Abscission of the affected leaves usually occurs within a few days to a week after the appearance of the blotches.

Twigs and stems are relatively flexible, slender, and deficient in woodiness.

In severe cases twigs die back from tips during winter.

The cortex of roots dies quickly and turns brown.

The effect of magnesium deficiency was first a grayish-green spotting, or mottling, later fading to a cream white and then changing to a fawn-colored brown. The discolored areas gradually assumed dull medium brown.

POTASH STARVATION

L. C. Hoffman, of the Ohio Agricultural Experiment Station, in an article reprinted from *Better Crops with Plant Food Magazine,* has the following to say concerning potash starvation in the greenhouse.

It is believed by plant physiologists that potassium does not combine with the plant tissue but remains largely dissolved in the sap and is easily transported throughout the plant. The first symptom of potash deficiency exhibited by the plant is a general slowing up in growth. This will continue and produce a stunted appearance in time. The color of the plant may become darker at first and then tend to become dull or ashen gray toward the edges of the leaves. The plants become more susceptible to disease and low yields are obtained. The old leaves at the base of the plants become affected first. As they collapse and die the potassium moves out during the dehydration process and is carried upward. Hence the tops of the plants remain green and continue to elongate slowly after the leaves at the base have died.

The symptoms of potash deficiency in the leaves of tomatoes and cucumbers are progressive in their development. In young leaves, when ample nitrogen is present the leaf-blade is often finely crinkled between the veins, and in tomatoes the edges are usually curved downward and inward, forming a partially rolled condition. As the leaves become older and somewhat larger, they tend to flatten. In a short time the margins of the leaves turn ashen gray and then yellowish in color. Small brown spots appear in the margins. These spots later become larger, unite, and form what is called "brown edge scorch," finally killing the entire margin. A brownish color appears mixed through the green in the web of the leaves, giving the center of the blades a bronze appearance. The leaves soon become harsh to the touch and brittle. The petioles of the leaves also are brittle and snap off cleanly with a light upward pressure.

Visual Deficiencies

In a reprint in the same magazine, distributed by the American Potash Institute, F. W. McElivice has the following to say. This quotation is taken from the summary.

In general, the visual deficiency symptoms for nitrogen (N) phosphorus (P) and potassium (K) for the plants studied may be summarized as follows:

1. *Nitrogen deficiency* produces a severe dwarfing of the plant and a uniform yellowing of all leaves. The young leaves begin to yellow very soon after the oldest leaves begin to turn. The affected leaves die slowly and remain attached to the plant for some time. The plant ceases to produce new growth soon after yellowing begins.

2. *Phosphorus deficiency* produces a severe dwarfing of the plant with most of the leaves remaining abnormally dark green. In severe cases the oldest turn grayish-green or sometimes purplish-green and later begin to turn yellow. The yellowing usually begins at the margin and progresses toward the petiole and the leaf usually drops before it becomes completely yellow. The plant ceases to produce new growth soon after yellowing begins.

3. *Potassium deficiency* usually produces only a slight dwarfing of the plant and the leaves remain normal dark green in color until affected by the characteristic potassium injury. The injury usually appears first on the oldest leaves when the margin and area between the veins turn yellow and the veins remain green. Later the leaf begins to turn brown and dies along the margin and in spots over the leaf. The leaves die slowly and remain attached to the plant for some time after dying.

Chrysanthemum Symptoms

An article entitled "Chrysanthemums Thrive in Sand Cultures," by H. Hill and M. B. Davis, of the Central Experimental Farm, Ottawa, Canada, gives the following:

The following plant symptoms have been found useful in determining the fertilizer requirements of chrysanthemums when growing in either soil or sand. As in many other plants the ratio between nitrogen and potassium is of particular importance in the feeding of the chrysanthemum, which gives an added advantage over a crop like tomatoes in that high-level feeding of both nitrogen and potassium can be practiced with a greater degree of safety since there are no fruits which might be affected with physiological disorders.

Whilst many a fairly good bloom has been produced on a chrysanthemum plant with almost one-half of its foliage gone from the base upward, there is no reason why such a condition of foliage should exist. The ill effects of high-nitrogen feeding are easily overcome by increasing the amount of potassium fed. As the nitrogen is increased, so should the potassium be increased. Chlorosis of the lower leaves, dropping of the lower leaves, curling and death all indicate either potassium starvation or nitrogen excess.

Deficient nitrogen, unlike excess of that element, produces leaves which do not burn or show marginal chlorosis. Here the leaves may be somewhat small, pale green to yellowish green, and in extreme cases show reddened veins, but the leaf always remains entire and not mottled or scorched.

The chrysanthemum is particularly susceptible to excess phosphorus feeding, and peculiarly enough, this is an element that many greenhouse men do use to excess in the form of bone meal and superphosphate. To the casual observer excess phosphorus symptoms resemble excess nitrogen symptoms, but there is a very distinct difference noticeable upon close examination. In the case of excess phosphorus feeding the trouble commences around the margins of the leaves in the form of a slight yellowing, as in the case of excess nitrogen feeding. This is very quickly followed by the appearance of maroon-red blotches following the margins rather closely and leaving the center of the leaf a normal green. This symptom is exceedingly valuable in the growing of chrysanthemums and should be carefully studied in contrast to the deficient potassium or excess nitrogen symptoms.

Lack of phosphorus is characterized by a great reduction in vigor, plants spindly, leaves small and sparse with internodes farther apart. In color, the leaves are at first a dull, deep green, with the older leaves becoming a dull reddish purple. The lower leaves which die from phosphorus starvation are reddish purple in color and not yellowish or light brown as in the case of excess nitrogen.

The symptoms described above refer to foliage conditions only, but quantity and quality of bloom are also greatly influenced by feeding practices. . . . High feeding of phosphorus even in the presence of ample potassium and nitrogen resulted in a marked decrease in the number of blossoms and some decrease in size. As might be expected, deficiency of either phosphorus or potassium brought about a marked reduction in the number and size of bloom.

One of the most outstanding features of these experiments was the effect of the feeding on the color of the bloom. In one variety which should normally produce bloom ocherous orange in color, the feeding of excess nitrogen resulted in the production of bloom

Empire yellow in color. The same result was produced by a reduction in the amount of potassium fed or by increasing the amount of phosphorus in the solution. Further increases of potassium intensified the ocherous orange, producing a more deeply pigmented bloom.

This same effect on color intensity was noted with another variety normally producing pink blossoms. With high nitrogen feeding, blooms almost pure white in color were produced; the same effect was produced with high phosphorus feeding. On the other hand, increasing the amount of potassium intensified the pink to a much deeper shade. In both varieties the production of a large number of blooms of good size and deep color was made possible by increased feeding of nitrogen, accompanied by a high feeding of potassium. It would appear that the development of a suitable intensity of bloom-color in chrysanthemums is dependent on an adequate supply of potassium, not only in total amount but in its relative concentration to nitrogen or phosphorus. The amount of nitrogen fed should not exceed twice that of potassium.

A careful study of the articles quoted in this chapter and accurate observation of your crop should give you the ability to determine just what element is deficient and should be added, or which one appears to be in excess of the plant requirement and should be counteracted. When this is determined, see that the solution is adjusted immediately by adding the proper amount of the salt required. Again we stress the fact that it is not necessary to use a multiplicity of salts. We have worked out our method to the point where we use only four main salts: calcium nitrate, $Ca(NO_3)_2$; potassium nitrate, KNO_3; monocalcium phosphate, $CaH_4(PO_4)_2$; and magnesium sulfate, $MgSO_4$. These four salts supply the nitrogen, potassium, phosphorus, magnesium, as well as calcium and sulfur. Since we use the fertilizer grade most of the minor elements with the possible exception of iron and manganese are present as impurities in sufficient quantities for the plant. Restricting ourselves to these four main salts enables us to buy in larger quantities thus getting a cheaper price. Furthermore, we do not have to store and keep track of a dozen different salts, and this again simplifies our problems.

CHAPTER XII

GENERAL CULTURAL CONDITIONS

Nutrient culture has the same problems of greenhouse operation as soil culture, and the methods are much alike. We will mention some of the differences as well as some similarities in the essential procedures.

In any method of growing crops it is extremely important that we use the finest seeds available. Particular care must be taken in selecting those strains which are intended for greenhouse use, in order to obtain a maximum crop possessing the characteristics demanded by the popular market.

SEEDLINGS

We have always made a practice of starting our seedlings or cuttings in the usual way in sand or soil. When they are ready for removal from the seedbed they are potted up and handled the same as if they were going to be grown in soil. When they attain the proper size to bench, we knock them out of the pots, lay them on screens, and, without too great water pressure, wash all the soil from the roots. They are then ready for planting in the nutrient benches. We usually transplant to the benches at the same time of year and use the same size of plants as though we were growing in soil. Simply scoop out a hollow in the cinders or gravel, spread the roots properly, and rake the material back in place around them. *Do not use force* in pressing the cinders or gravel around the roots or you may injure them. We have *not* found it necessary to use shading on the houses after transplanting. Once the plants take hold they will develop somewhat more rapidly than if grown in soil. As they increase in size they should be staked and tied as in soil culture. If you prefer, the seeds can be planted in sand, keeping them wet with ordinary water until germination takes place, after which the seedlings can be watered with the regular nutrient solution. When they attain the right size they can be transplanted directly into the cinder or gravel benches at the cor-

115

rect spacing for growing. In this way you save the time and expense of potting and shifting as well as the trouble of washing the soil from the roots. You will probably save a few days' time and also gain some extra days in the development of your plants as there is no set-back at the time of transplanting. One of the chief advantages of starting seeds and cuttings in sand is that one of the greatest sources of diseases is avoided since the presence of soil naturally increases the possibility of infection.

CUTTINGS

With a crop such as carnations grown from cuttings, the rooted cuttings can be planted directly in the nutrient benches spaced 2 inches apart each way, and when of proper size they may be transplanted to the regular spacing. See Fig. 27. This too saves time and avoids the usual setback incident to transplanting. If you buy carnation stock plants instead of growing your own cuttings, be sure to specify pot-grown plants as otherwise too much of the root system is lost. We usually plant carnations and mums at the same distances as for soil culture because of the increased growth we obtain with nutrients. Roses are spaced 10 inches each way instead of 12 inches as ordinarily done in soil benches. Tomatoes are planted in two rows in a 3½-foot bench and spaced 12 inches in the row instead of the customary 14 inches apart.

NEW ROSE STOCK

With new budded rose stock, we heel in the plants in the nutrient bench and cover with cloth to retain the moisture. See Fig. 28. This keeps the outer bark soft and makes them break more freely. Just as with soil culture, we find that budded stock is worth the extra cost because the crop comes in sooner and there are more flowers per plant.

HUMIDITY

Naturally houses devoted to nutrient culture have less humidity than houses devoted to soil culture. This arises from the fact that with soil a great deal of water runs through the benches and is absorbed in the ground underneath. This results in an excess of moisture immediately after the benches are watered and is usually followed by a deficiency of moisture as the benches dry out. It is this variation of humidity that is largely responsible for many of our plant diseases such as mildew and black spot on roses, leaf mold on tomatoes, and

FIG. 27. Rooted carnation cuttings planted direct from cutting bench into nutrient bench, thus eliminating potting, shifting, and washing soil from roots. These plants when of proper size will be shifted direct to the final nutrient bench. Fountain pen shows relative distance in row.

FIG. 28. This shows how new budded rose stock is handled. Note dormant buds (light space center foreground) heeled-in in cinders fed with nutrients, also black cloth (upper right) used to cover buds to retain moisture and heat, and mass of foliage (upper left) indicating well-started buds ready to be transplanted to permanent place in nutrient bench.

rust on carnations. Houses in which cool-temperatured crops are grown do not show the difficulties that we have with the warm-temperatured crops.

Crops such as roses require a humidity of 70. Most experienced growers can feel when the humidity is right, but if you are not sure, it should be measured. This can be done by placing, in a current of air, a wet-and-dry-bulb thermometer which can be purchased from any regular supply house. A chart of temperatures and humidity with full directions usually accompanies it. If the humidity is low, it may be adjusted by wetting down the walks daily or as needed. The more steam pipes needed to maintain the correct temperature, the more likely it is that the humidity should be increased.

SYRINGING

Syringing may be done in the same manner as with soil-grown plants, if they are planted in cinders or gravel. Once the plants are established they will not pull out even if a water pressure of 120 pounds is used. Each day a certain amount of water evaporates from the tank and benches so that in a short time the solution in the tank is low enough to permit syringing. Much of the water used in syringing falls on the benches and will flow back into the nutrient tank. Until you become accustomed to the amount of water to be used, watch the tank carefully to see that it does not overflow. It may be necessary to syringe only one or two benches at a time. Syringing keeps the outer bark soft and the plants will break better. Unless the solution-tank is being allowed to get low for syringing, it should be filled each day to the level which you originally marked in order to keep the benches uniformly full and to maintain the solution at a constant concentration.

SPRAYING

Some growers may have a question about sprays and fumigants. We have found no difference between soil culture and nutrient culture in this respect. There may be some sprays that might get into the nutrient solution by falling on the cinders, but we have experienced no such difficulty.* We have used nicotine, Selocide, Loro, Multicide, arsenate of lead, Paris green, and Cyclonox as well as various pyreth-

---

* Both Purdue and Ohio State recommend filling the benches with clear tap water before spraying and emptying them afterwards before again feeding the solution. This would probably avoid any possibility of root injury.

rum and derris sprays without any apparent injury. The same commercial fumigants may be used. We have used nicotine and Cyanogas without any difficulty. The only injury we ever noted was with nicotine, when it was dissolved in the nutrient solution in a concentration of 1-1,000 to get rid of rose midge. This destroyed the rose midge and many of the roots, but the plants recovered. Probably if a lower concentration of Nicofume or if nicotine sulfate had been used the midge would have been destroyed with no resulting injury to the root. We mention this difficulty so that you will understand that you need to be careful if you experiment with unknown chemicals in the nutrients. We have never experienced any difficulty when nicotine was used as a regular spray.

Temperatures

As to temperatures, the range is handled the same as for soil. For cool crops such as carnations, mums, snaps, peas, and calendula, maintain the house at 50° at night, 55° on cloudy days, and 58° on sunny days. (Stocks can be kept as low as 40°.) For warm crops such as roses, gardenias, and tomatoes hold the temperature at 60° at night, 65° on cloudy days, and from 68° or 70° to 75° on very bright days.

Leaching

For several months after you start a new bench or house in nutrients you will probably find that your solution changes quite rapidly and needs to have certain elements replaced frequently. This is possibly due to the fact that, until the material used as fill in the benches is thoroughly impregnated with the solution, some of the salts are held in the benches. After this period the solution will vary only to the extent that the plants extract the nutrients from it.

There is another point on which we wish to caution you. There may be times when you will want to change crops in a house or make a radical change in the solution formula. In such cases it is not necessary to change the gravel or cinders, but it is important that you thoroughly leach them by filling the benches with ordinary tap water, allowing it to stand a couple of days, and then draining it off. Repeat this operation several times, particularly if the previous solution has been carried with a radically different concentration of any of the salts to be used in the new solution. It appears that the cinders or gravel have a tendency to hold or retain some of the highly concentrated salts, and this will throw off the balance of the new formula.

If you have had any serious infection similar to the soil diseases, or if the crop you intend to grow is one which is particularly susceptible to soil diseases, we recommend that you sterilize the old cinders or gravel just as you did when starting the system originally. This can be done easily and inexpensively by using acid or formaldehyde.* Remember that formaldehyde must not be used if there are any growing plants that might come in contact with its fumes and so be injured.

COMPARATIVE COSTS

It is difficult to compare the exact cost of fertilizer used on soil-grown plants with the cost of the fertilizer salts used in nutrient culture. With soil, both chemical fertilizers and manures are used, and considerable labor is involved in mulching with manure, whereas with nutrient culture only chemicals are used and there is no appreciable extra cost in applying additional amounts with the varying seasons. We believe that a satisfactory way is to give the exact cost of the nutrient salts used for a given area and let each grower make his own comparison for a similar area. For a six-month period, the average cost per month for nutrient salts to supply a range of glass covering a ground area of 40,000 square feet (approximately 1 acre) was $24.15. The cost per month was as follows: September, $22.66; October, $26.41; November, $24.49; December, $27.66; January, $28.03; February, $15.75; or a total of $145. You will notice that the month of February used only $15.75 for this area. This was probably due to decreasing the potassium concentration in the solution on account of longer brighter days which were then commencing to make their influence felt. During this same six-month period on a like area of soil-grown roses the average cost per month, including the labor cost of mulching, was $20.58 for manure and $15 for commercial fertilizers such as ammonium sulfate and Vigoro. This represents an average saving each month of this period of $11.43.

COMPARATIVE PRODUCTION

It would not be fair to compare costs without considering the production record of the same areas. Our records indicate that with roses there is no phenomenal increase in quantity but quality was definitely better. Nutrient-grown "Briarcliff" roses produced one and

---

* Both formaldehyde and acid can probably be used in a concentration of 1-100, although we ordinarily use sulfuric acid in a concentration of 1-150.

one-half more flowers per plant than soil-grown "Briarcliff" over this six-month period. However, a similar variety "Better Times" produced about one flower per plant less in nutrients than in soil. Even though the production per plant of roses grown in nutrients was not much greater than the production per plant in soil, the house produced 20 per cent more flowers because the plants are set out with 20 per cent less space per plant for the nutrient-culture method. It is interesting to note that at the present time (two months later) the production of nutrient-grown "Better Times" has equalled and is rapidly exceeding that of the soil-grown "Better Times." We believe this is due to the fact that we can and do vary the nitrogen-potassium balance in the solution so that it agrees with the changing light conditions and we are not able to make such rapid changes for our soil-grown plants.

With tomatoes we had no check test soil benches for comparison, but our crop appeared to be no greater than the average good grower would obtain in soil. Tomatoes responded remarkably well to nutrient culture in that the quality of the fruit could be changed almost completely by varying the chemicals in the solution, as was seen by the alteration in water content as soon as the nitrogen-potassium balance was changed. This was our first attempt to grow tomatoes in any way, but several reliable and experienced growers who watched the crop critically remarked that the fruit was exceptionally uniform and of high quality.

Chrysanthemums and stocks were of fine quality when grown in nutrients. The color was exceptionally good but the production was not materially increased. In the case of stocks the crop was brought in two weeks earlier than those grown in soil and this resulted in obtaining a much better price on the market. Chrysanthemums showed very little difference over those grown in soil.

Carnations seem to be the crop which to date has responded best to nutrient culture. Our first year's production was practically three times greater than with our soil-grown plants. This comparison is not scientifically accurate as such crops would be grown experimentally, since we did not grow the same varieties in both soil and nutrients and the soil-grown plants were benched three weeks later than the nutrient-grown plants. However, there was such a tremendous difference in production that we are certain much of the increase can be credited to nutrient culture rather than to the variety or time of benching. The varieties used in both cultures were high-quality tested commercial ones. This difference of three to one can hardly be overlooked or minimized. The production in nutrient solutions was slightly over twenty blooms per plant. The quality of bloom was such that they always brought top price on the market.

Labor Advantages

One of the greatest advantages of nutrient culture is the saving of labor costs. Those men who actually do the growing may be reduced by one-third in comparison with the number required in soil growing. This saving results primarily by eliminating the necessity of hand watering, mulching, weeding, and cultivating. Less repair labor is needed to keep the houses in good shape. Under nutrient-culture methods one good grower can take care of approximately 15,000 rose plants or 30,000 carnation plants, once they are established in the benches. It takes on the average only 35 hours per month to test, feed, and apply minor elements in the way we recommend over an area of 40,000 square feet of ground. This is slightly more than one hour per day. Compare this with the time required to water by hand, mulch, cultivate, and weed a similar area when plants are grown in soil.

In comparing the results we have obtained on large-scale nutrient-culture production with the difficulties and problems that have arisen on some of the smaller installations which we have observed, we believe that our success has been largely due to the fact that we were working on a large scale rather than to any superior knowledge on our part. See Fig. 29. Minor errors in calculation and in regularity of feeding become gross errors when applied to small experimental plots. It is for that reason that we urge you to have confidence in this method and give it a trial on such a basis as will assure your success. We firmly believe that any good grower in soil need have no fear or misgiving about his ability to produce a better than average crop in his first year.

We appreciate that this method of growing has not been readily accepted by many prominent growers. There are some who apparently would discredit it; but considering the success we have had and the definite advantages it offers, we do not hesitate to say that we believe it will be adopted or adapted in a great many large commercial establishments within the next five years. The scientific research departments of our many fine agricultural experiment stations have contributed the groundwork and have established the practical application of the method. We believe that now is the time for practical commercial growers to continue the good work and in this way make

FIG. 29. Construction of benches in converting two more houses to nutrient culture at the Wholesale Floral Company, Aurora, Illinois. This will make a total of eleven houses (about two acres) in successful nutrient culture.

even greater contribution to the business of growing flowers and vegetables profitably. The commercial grower should recognize that his greatest opportunity for profitable production lies in establishing a lower cost, a higher quality, and thus a larger market because he must compete with cheaper outdoor crops. True economy depends not upon a limited production of high-cost products which can be sold only to a limited group, but upon a high-class product grown at a reasonable cost and sold to the mass of people.

Heretofore it required endless search through innumerable volumes of scientific documents to unearth the simple facts and formulas necessary to use this method of growing. Often, when the facts were brought to light, they were in such form that the layman could not understand and apply them. This was not due to a desire for secrecy on the part of the scientific investigators but rather to the fact that in their work they must first of all be technically accurate, and this often leads to unusual terminology. Their facts and data were readily understood by their co-workers, but to the layman were unintelligible. Its very complexity and formidableness discouraged many growers who we believe otherwise would have tried it long ago. We are sure that the simple detailed facts given herein will enable others to advance with confidence on the foundation already established. There is plenty of room for improvement in both method and practice, and that improvement will undoubtedly come through the practical grower who steps out fearlessly and tries and experiments and improves as he goes along. We trust that in some small measure we have shown the way, and that this volume will encourage such progressive men to work on these unsolved problems for the ultimate good of the entire industry.

SOURCES OF EQUIPMENT AND MATERIALS

We give the following list of manufacturers and chemical supply houses simply for the convenience of those who may not know just where these things may be purchased. In no sense do we mean to infer that other sources are not reliable. In fact, we suggest that you first attempt to locate a local supply, as in so doing you will save on transportation charges and in addition will have the benefit of local service if needed.

WATERPROOFING MATERIALS

Asphalt emulsions United Laboratories, Cleveland, Ohio.
Korite   Standard Oil of Indiana, Chicago, Illinois.

MOTOR-DRIVEN PUMPS

Yeomans Brothers Pump Company, 1433 Dayton St., Chicago, Illinois.
Fairbanks-Morse Company, Michigan Avenue, Chicago, Illinois.
American Well Works, Aurora, Illinois.
Deming Pump Company, Salem, Ohio.

ELECTRICAL EQUIPMENT

Sangamo Electric Company, Springfield, Illinois.
General Electric Company, Schenectady, New York.
Cutler-Hammer Company, 116 North Green Street, Chicago, Illinois.

TESTING KITS

Purdue University, Agronomy Department, Lafayette, Indiana.
Urbana Laboratories, Urbana, Illinois.
La Motte Chemical Products Company, Baltimore, Maryland.

CHEMICAL BALANCES

The Torsion Balance Company, 228 North La Salle Street, Chicago, Illinois.
E. H. Sargent, Chicago, Illinois.
Eimer and Amend, Third Avenue and 18th Street, New York City.

ACIDS AND LABORATORY SUPPLIES

Central Chemical, 4100 S. Ashland Ave., Chicago, Illinois.
Central Scientific Company, Chicago, Illinois.

Fertilizer Chemicals (Salts)

Armour and Company (offices in principal cities), Chicago, Illinois.
Synthetic Nitrogen Products Company, 85 Madison Avenue,
New York City.
Monsanto Chemical Company, St. Louis, Missouri.
Victor Chemical Works, 141 West Jackson Blvd., Chicago, Illinois.
Baugh and Sons Company, Baltimore, Maryland.
Dow Chemical Company, Midland, Michigan.
F. W. Berk and Company, 420 Lexington Avenue, New York City.
Central Chemical, 4100 S. Ashland Ave., Chicago, Illinois.
McKesson & Robbins, Inc., 540 W. Randolph St., Chicago, Illinois.
Mallinckrodt Chemical Works, St. Louis, Missouri.
Merck and Company, New York City.

BIBLIOGRAPHY

For those who wish to read and study more of the extensive work on nutrient culture and allied subjects we are listing some of the more recent bulletins, books, and magazine references. Much has been written and undoubtedly much more will be written on the sensational side of this subject. We have tried to include those articles from authoritative sources which we believe will add to your fund of knowledge. The omission of a reference does not mean that it is of a questionable character or unreliable. We have not attempted to go back beyond 1936 in our periodical references as ideas and methods are changing so rapidly that it would not be feasible to list all articles. For those who wish to study more of the history of this fascinating subject we refer you to the *Reader's Guide to Periodical Literature* under "Plants, Nutrition of," for various years.

BOOKS

Soilless Growth of Plants, ELLIS and SWANEY, Reinhold Publishing Corporation, New York City. $2.75. 160 pp.
Botany, L. H. BAILEY, The Macmillan Company, New York City.
A Textbook of Botany, COULTER, BARNES, and COWLES, The American Book Company, New York City.
Elements of Botany, HOLMAN and ROBBINS, John Wiley & Sons, New York City.
Plant Physiology, EDWIN C. MILLER, McGraw-Hill Book Company, New York City.
Principles of Plant Growth, WILFRED ROBBINS, John Wiley & Sons, New York City.
A Textbook of Chemistry, W. A. NOYES, Henry Holt and Company, New York City.
Photometric Chemical Analysis, JOHN H. YOE, John Wiley & Sons, New York City.
Plant Physiology, MEYER and ANDERSON, D. Van Nostrand Company, New York City.

BULLETINS

"Greenhouse Culture of Carnations in Sand," BIEKART and CONNORS, *New Jersey Agriculture Experiment Station Bulletin* 588, 1935.
"Nutrient Solution Methods of Greenhouse Crop Production," WITHROW and BIEBEL, *Purdue University Agriculture Experiment Station Circular* 232. Revised, 1938.
"Experiments in Water Cultures," HOAGLAND and ARNON, University of California Agriculture Experiment Station, 1938.

United States Department of Agriculture Technical Bulletin 340, J. E. McMURTREY, 1933.

"Methods of Growing Plants in Solution and Sand Cultures," SHIVE and ROBBINS, *New Jersey Agriculture Experiment Station Bulletin* 636, 1937.

"The Use of Rapid Tests on Soils and Plants as Aids to Determining Fertilizer Needs," THORNTON, CONNER, and FRASER, *Purdue University Agriculture Experiment Station Bulletin* 204, 1936.

"The Water Culture Method for Growing Plants without Soil," HOAGLAND and ARNON, *University of California Agriculture Experiment Station Bulletin* 347, 1938.

"Potash Starvation in the Greenhouse," I. C. HOFFMAN, Ohio Agricultural Experiment Station, Wooster, Ohio.*

"Tomatoes and Cucumbers Reveal Diet Needs," I. C. HOFFMAN, Ohio Agricultural Experiment Station, Wooster, Ohio.*

"Flower Symptoms Warn of Food Deficiency," E. W. McELWEE, Alabama Polytechnic Institute.*

"Chrysanthemums Thrive in Sand Cultures," HILL and DAVIS, Central Experimental Farm, Ottawa, Ontario, Canada.

"Growing Plants in Water Solutions," E. E. DeTURK, University of Illinois Department of Agronomy, Agricultural Experiment Station.

"Bibliography of References to the Literature on 'The Minor Elements and Their Relation to Plant and Animal Nutrition,'" L. G. WILLIS, Chilean Nitrate Educational Bureau, Inc., 120 Broadway, New York City. $1.00.

"Gravel and Cinder Culture for Greenhouse Flowering Crops," ARNOLD WAGNER, Ohio State University Division of Floriculture, 13 pp., mimeographed, 1939.

Various mimeographed *Bulletins* by "Roses, Incorporated," published in Columbus, Ohio. See especially *Bulletin* 7. June, 1938; and 11, October, 1938.

Ohio Florists Association Monthly Bulletin 95, August, 1937; and 106, July, 1938.

"Chemical Gardens and How to Care for Them," Chemical Garden Company, 555 Asbury Avenue, Evanston, Illinois, 1938. $0.25.

"Tank Farming," ROY V. INGRAM, California Tank Farming Study Group, 754 East 104th Street, Los Angeles, California, 1937. $1.00.

PERIODICALS

"Heating of Liquid Culture Media for Tomato Production," GERICKE and TAVERNETTI, *Agricultural Engineering*, 17:141-2, April, 1936.

"Crops Grown without Soil," *American Fertilizer*, April 13, 1936.

"A New Three Salt Solution for Plant Cultures," LIVINGSTON and TOTTINGHAM, *American Journal of Botany*, 5:337-46, 1918.

"Changes in Hydrogen Ion Concentration of Culture Solutions Containing Nitrate and Ammonium Nitrogen," TRELEASE and TRELEASE, *American Journal of Botany*, 22:520-42, 1935.

"The Possibilities of Sand Culture for Research and Commercial Work in Horticulture," W. R. ROBBINS, American Society of Horticultural Science.

"Constant Rates of Continuous Solution Renewal for Plants in Water Cultures," SHIVE and STAHL, *Botanical Gazette*, 84:317-23, 1927.

* These three bulletins are distributed by American Potash Institute, Inc., Midwest Office, Life Building, Lafayette, Indiana.

"Effects of Nutrient Concentration on Anatomy, Metabolism and Bud Abscission of Sweet Peas," NIGHTINGALE and FARNHAM, *Botanical Gazette,* 97:477-517, 1936.

"Experiments with a New Greenhouse Bench," FARNHAM and KREUGER, *Florists Review,* p. 14, June 11, 1938.

"Experiments in Adopting Water Culture to Commercial Crops," GERICKE, *Florists Review,* pp. 13-15, Oct. 22, 1936.

"Growing Plants in Nutrient Solutions," J. W. SHIVE. *Flower Grower,* March, 1938.

"Automatically Operated Sand Culture Equipment," F. M. EATON. *Journal of Agricultural Research,* 53:433-44, 1936.

"A Subirrigation Method of Supplying Nutrients to Plants Growing under Commercial and Experimental Conditions," WITHROW and BIEBEL, *Journal of Agricultural Research,* 53:693-702, 1936.

"A Quantitiative Chemical and Physiological Study of Nutrient Solutions for Plant Culture," W. E. TOTTINGHAM, *Physiological Research,* 1:133-245, 1914.

"A Study of Physiological Balance in Nutrient Media," J. W. SHIVE, *Physiological Research,* 1:1327-97, 1914.

"Relation of Nutrient Salt Concentration to Growth of the Tomato and to the Incidence of Blossom End Rot of the Fruit," *Plant Physiology,* 12:21-50, 1937.

"Liquid Culture Media." W. F. GERICKE, *Science,* Feb. 12, 1937.

"Plants Grown in Sand Given Mineral Nutrients in Solution," *Science News Letter,* p. 362, June 4, 1938.

"Nutritional Studies with Chrysanthemums, HILL and DAVIS, *Scientific Agriculture,* 15:110-24, 1934.

"Plants by Liquid Culture," GREAVES and CARPENTER (formulas, instruction and suggestions), *Scientific American,* 160:5-7, January, 1939.

"What is Soil?" W. F. GERICKE, *Science,* n. s. 88:568-9, Dec. 16, 1938.

"Plants Grown in Sand," *Science News Letter,* 33:362, June 4, 1938.

"Hydroponic Gardening," *House and Garden,* p. 74, November, 1938.

"Truth about Tank Farming," *Popular Mechanics,* 70:232-5, August, 1938.

"Gardening without Dirt," *Ladies' Home Journal,* 55:85, January, 1938.

"You Can Try It Yourself, Vegetable Growing Without Soil," F. J. TAYLOR, *Saturday Evening Post,* 211:14-15, Aug. 20, 1938.

"Wake Island's Soilless Farm Well under Way," *Science News Letter,* 33:381, June 11, 1938.

"Miracle Plants Grow in Liquid," P. MERRIMAN, *Popular Mechanics,* 69:594-6, April, 1938.

RECORD SHEET SHOWING CONDITION OF SOLUTION AND AMOUNT OF SALTS ADDED

Date	Tank No.		PPM. of Element by Testing Solution							Salt Used	Grams Added to Tank
			N	K	Mg	P	Fe	Ca	pH		
3/15	1	Required	300	250	60	70	✓	✓	5.6	$Ca(NO_3)_2$	2409
		Found (−)	250	200	59	35	✓	✓	5.6	KNO_3	1500
		Replaced	50	50	1	35	✓	✓	✓	$MgSO_4$	none
										$CaH_4(PO_4)_2$	1960
		Required									
		Found (−)									
		Replaced									
		Required									
		Found (−)									
		Replaced									

132

RECORD SHEET SHOWING CONDITION OF SOLUTION AND AMOUNT OF SALTS ADDED

Date	Tank No.		PPM. of Element by Testing Solution								Salt Used	Grams Added to Tank
			N	K	Mg	P	Fe	Ca	pH			
		Required										
		Found (−)										
		Replaced										
		Required										
		Found (−)										
		Replaced										
		Required										
		Found (−)										
		Replaced										

RECORD SHEET SHOWING CONDITION OF SOLUTION AND AMOUNT OF SALTS ADDED

Date	Tank No.		PPM. of Element by Testing Solution								Salt Used	Grams Added to Tank
			N	K	Mg	P	Fe	Ca	pH			
		Required										
		Found (−)										
		Replaced										
		Required										
		Found (−)										
		Replaced										
		Required										
		Found (−)										
		Replaced										

RECORD SHEET SHOWING CONDITION OF SOLUTION AND AMOUNT OF SALTS ADDED

Date	Tank No.		PPM. of Element by Testing Solution							Salt Used	Grams Added to Tank
			N	K	Mg	P	Fe	Ca	pH		
		Required									
		Found (−)									
		Replaced									
		Required									
		Found (−)									
		Replaced									
		Required									
		Found (−)									
		Replaced									

RECORD SHEET SHOWING COMPOSITION OF FORMULA AND AMOUNT OF SALTS USED

Tank　　　　Capacity in Liters　　　　Crop Grown　　　　Date

Salt Used	Millimoles Required by Formula	Element Supplied	PPM. in Solution	Grams per Molecule	Grams Required	Grams to Give 1 ppm.
Ca(NO$_3$)$_2$	6	N	168	180	12,204	73

RECORD SHEET SHOWING COMPOSITION OF FORMULA AND AMOUNT OF SALTS USED

Tank   Capacity in Liters   Crop Grown   Date

Salt Used	Millimoles Required by Formula	Element Supplied	PPM. in Solution	Grams per Molecule	Grams Required	Grams to Give 1 ppm.

RECORD SHEET SHOWING COMPOSITION OF FORMULA AND AMOUNT OF SALTS USED

Tank   Capacity in Liters   Crop Grown   Date

Salt Used	Millimoles Required by Formula	Element Supplied	PPM. in Solution	Grams per Molecule	Grams Required	Grams to Give 1 ppm.

DAILY RECORD SHEET SHOWING CROP AND WEATHER CONDITIONS

Date	Temperature		Weather		Condition of Crop			Flowers Cut	
	Outside	Inside	Sunny	Cloudy	Poor	Fair	Fine		
3/15	52°	62°	✓				✓	1500	

DAILY RECORD SHEET SHOWING CROP AND WEATHER CONDITIONS

Date	Temperature		Weather		Condition of Crop			Flowers Cut	
	Outside	Inside	Sunny	Cloudy	Poor	Fair	Fine		

DAILY RECORD SHEET SHOWING CROP AND WEATHER CONDITIONS

Date	Temperature		Weather		Condition of Crop			Flowers Cut	
	Outside	Inside	Sunny	Cloudy	Poor	Fair	Fine		

DAILY RECORD SHEET SHOWING CROP AND WEATHER CONDITIONS

Date	Temperature		Weather		Condition of Crop			Flowers Cut	
	Outside	Inside	Sunny	Cloudy	Poor	Fair	Fine		

INDEX AND GLOSSARY

A star (*) indicates that the mentioned item is illustrated on the page number cited. **Boldface** indicates definition.

143

Benches, New Jersey Bulletin on, 22
 photograph of, *21
 starting new crop in, leaching, 120
 V trough for, *18, *20
 wooden, 17-22
  diagram of, *18
  waterproofing, 19
Bench-fill: any medium used to support the root system of the plant such as cinders, gravel, and sand.
Biekart, H. M., bench-fill, 26
 carnation quality in nutrients, 12
 large-scale sand culture, 3
Blake, M. A., deficiency symptoms, 109-111
Boron, 49, 86, 108
 deficiency symptom, 86, 108
 function of, 86
 source of, 49
Box, window, 31
Break: frequently used by greenhouse men in referring to the tendency of dormant buds starting in to new growth, especially roses and other hardwooded crops.
Bromocresol green, 92
Bromothymol blue, 91, 92
Burn: an injury to plant tissue having the appearance of destruction by heat, usually brown and dry and penetrating both sides of leaves.

C

Calcium, 47, 49, 50, 84, 101, 103, 108, 109, 110, 111
 deficiency, 84, 108, 109, 110, 111
 function of, 84
 relation to nitrogen, 84
 salts of, calcium chloride, 47
  calcium nitrate, 47, 49
  calcium phosphate, 47, 49, 50
  calcium sulfate, 47
 table showing parts per million in testing, 103
 testing for, 101, 103
California Experiment Station, 5, 12

Cambium layer, location of, 76
Capacity, of bench, 15
 of box, 30
 relative, of tank and bench, 15
 small-scale equipment, 30-32
Carbohydrates, manufacture of, *see* Photosynthesis
Carbon, 86
 plant need of, 86
 source of, 86
Carbon dioxide, 75
 function in photosynthesis, 75
 liberation of, 75
 source of, 75
Carnations, 66-68, 122
 chart, for nitrogen, *66
  for potassium, *67
 increased production, 122
 leaf test, 68
Catalytic agent, definition of, 42
Caulk: to fill large cracks with oakum or other material.
Caulk, 14
Cell, 79-81
 composition of, 80
 definition of, 79
 function of, 81
 growth of, 80, 81
 protoplasm, 80
Chadwick, L. C., Ohio State University. Dichotomous key of deficiencies, 106-108
Chemical salts, *see* Salts
Chemicals, fertilizer grade, 39, 40, 42, 46, 47, 48, 52, 70, 71, 128
 analysis of, 48-52
 compound, *see* Compound
 detrimental, 40, 46, 47, 70, 71
 impurities, 39, 42, 47
 source of, 47, 48, 128
Chemiculture: word coined to describe water culture or hydroponics.
Chemiculture, 1
Chlorophenol red, 92
Chlorophyll, 75, 78
 definition of, 75
 function of, 75, 78
 relation of, to photosynthesis, 75
Chloroplasts, 80

Respiration: the process by which plants absorb oxygen and give off carbon dioxide. (Do not confuse this with photosynthesis.)
Root: the portion of a plant, usually subterranean, which serves to anchor it and also acts as an organ of absorption, conduction, aeration, and food storage.

Root hairs: a fine outgrowth from an epidermal cell at the tip of a root, through which roots absorb water and nutrients.

S

Sand culture: usually applied to the method which uses sand or other fine media to anchor the plants, and in which the solution is applied on the surface and allowed to percolate through.
Scald: any one of several parasitic diseases, causing a burning or browning of plant tissues, which develop as a result of high temperatures, intense sunlight, or chemical deficiencies or excesses.
Silica: a very fine, clean, quartz sand.
Soilless agriculture: a term that may be applied to any method of supplying chemical nutrients in the absence of soil.